COUNTER-TERRORISM EQUIPMENT

GREENHILL MILITARY MANUALS

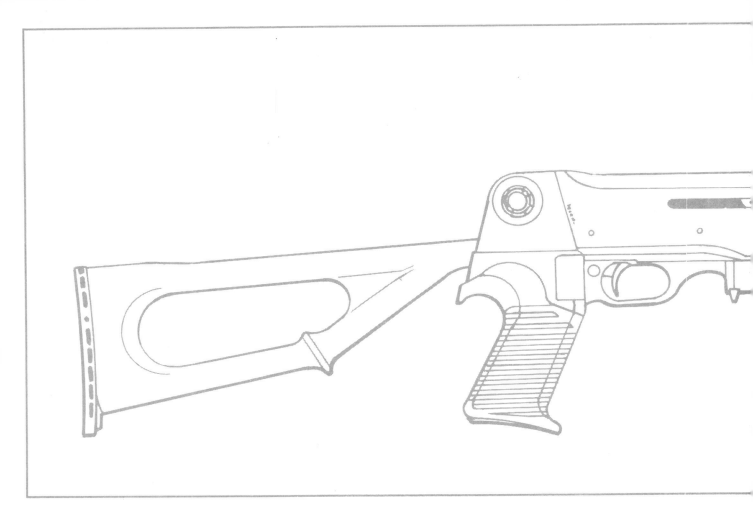

COUNTER-TERRORISM EQUIPMENT

IAN V. HOGG

ILLUSTRATED BY RAY HUTCHINS

GREENHILL MILITARY MANUALS

Greenhill Books, London
Stackpole Books, Pennsylvania

Counter -Terrorism Equipment
first published 1997 by
Greenhill Books, Lionel Leventhal Limited, Park House
1, Russell Gardens, London NW11 9NN
and
Stackpole Books, 5067 Ritter Road, Mechanicsburg, PA 17055, USA

British Library Cataloguing in Publication Data
Hogg, Ian V. (Ian Vernon), 1926 -
Counter-terrorism equipment. - (Greenhill Military Manuals)
I. Counterinsurgency - Equipment and supplies
2. Counterinsurgency - Technological innovations 3. Military supplies
I. Title II. Hutchins, Ray
355.8
ISBN 1-85367-267-X

Library of Congress Cataloging in Publication Data
Hogg, Ian., 1926 -
Counter-terrorism equipment / by Ian V. Hogg;
illustrated by Ray Hutchins.
144p. 15cm. -- (Greenhill military manuals; 10)
ISBN 1-85367-267-X
1. Police--Special weapons and tactics units--Equipment and supplies.
2. Terrorism--Prevention--Equipment and supplies.
1. Title. 11. Series.
HV8080.S64H64 1997
363.3'2'028--dc21
96-39715 CIP

Typeset by Merlin Publications
Printed and bound in Great Britain by
The Bath Press

Introduction

The fight against terrorism occupies tens of thousands of men and women 24 hours a day, 365 days a year and shows no sign of slackening. The terrorists are getting more numerous - and, more technical. Once it was sufficient for the police to use short-wave radios; now they need to use ultra-high frequency radios and complex encryption systems in order to keep their communications confidential. Then, the constable carried a bulls-eye lantern and a wooden truncheon; now he carries an expensive night vision device and a side-handle plastic baton that needs a 64-page manual of instruction and a two-week course before he can use it.

Police and security forces have moved, as with military forces, in the direction of the 'force multiplier', the weapon or device which increases the effectiveness of the individual to the level which would have required four or five individuals years ago. In the case of the military this usually means a more effective weapon, but in the case of police and security forces it can be one of many devices and is very rarely a high-technology weapon.

The police and security forces have a duty to prevent crime and so they look with favour upon the various technical developments applied to keeping the wrong people out, where they have no business to be, and allowing the right people in.

They have a duty to counter terrorism, and for this they need information about their area; they can best do this by looking at the area and studying its people to detect those who are up to no good. This 'surveillance' needs to be carried out by day and by night, and gives rise to a vast array of electronic and optical devices for seeing in the dark, seeing over long distances, detecting movement.

Having detected terrorist movement the police and security forces must move against them, and for this they need vehicles; ordinary vehicles may do well enough for most of the time, but they need specialised vehicles when they are confronted with severe terrorism and explosives, to avoid being shot at or blown up.

And with the terrorist introduced into the scene, we have the bomb threat, something which affects us all. The terrorist bomb is not something which your average police or security man can do very much about; it requires a particular kind of man with a particular kind of expertise to walk out to a suspected package and, having decided that yes, it is indeed a highly unstable bomb, proceed to render it safe. And in order to reduce the risk to that man as much as possible, highly ingenious devices have been developed to allow him to do a great deal of his dangerous work at a respectful distance from the suspect article.

This book, therefore, is about some of the many devices, gadgets, instruments, call them what you will, which the present-day police or security officer has at his disposal. Please understand that this is not an exhaustive catalogue of all such equipment; that would run to well over a thousand pages. Nor is it a detailed exposition of how these devices work and, by extension, how they can be evaded; this is not a terrorist's handbook, and there is nothing in here which cannot be found on the shelves of a good public library. Nor is it a fearless exposé of the cutting edge of technology; most of the items shown here have been available for some years, and in some cases we have deliberately not shown the latest version. It is simply a survey of a little-known but extremely busy and interesting field of activity, a survey which sets out to show that, in spite of popular jibes about P.C.Plod and the Keystone Cops, the police and security forces of today have some extremely sophisticated technology at their beck and call and know just how to use it to the best effect.

It might also go some way to answering the frequently-asked question of why the police and security forces need money; it will show that they have rather more than handcuffs and notebooks to buy. (Indeed, at the present moment, the police and security market is probably worth more in day-to-day business than the military market.) But do not immediately visit your local police station and ask to see their water-cannon; they are unlikely to have one. Not every force needs every piece of equipment shown here; a mid-city force would have little use for a radar capable of seeing 50 kilometres across a desert. But as an indication of the lengths to which police and security forces now have to go to keep ahead of the evildoers, the following pages may prove surprising.

Contents

The Future

The future is hard to determine because police and security forces are largely reactive; they can only move effectively after the terrorist has committed an offence. And therefore the direction in which the police and security forces are going can only be determined by the direction the terrorists take. If they use cellular telephones, then the police must obtain interception devices, if they adopt the aeroplane, then the police must adopt aircraft also.

With a degree of forethought, the security forces can be pro-active; they can move before the terrorist does and be waiting when he gets to that level of technology. It would be an unwise terrorist, for example, who would place any reliance on the secrecy of any form of electronic communication today, because interception equipment exists to deal with anything that uses electronic signals - telephones, radios, pagers, facsimile machines, car phones - and had existed for several years before the signalling equipment became popular. But, it takes a very prescient police officer to sanction the purchase of equipment which might lie dormant for a year or two before the need which he has foreseen actually arises.

One must also take in account the delaying tactics employed by those of 'liberal' thought. As fast as a new device is requested by the forces of law and order, just as fast do the protectors of liberty denounce it. CS gas has been in use world-wide for sixty years or so, but when the British police contemplate introducing it as a self-defence measure the air is filled with tales of how CS causes cancer, miscarriages, dandruff and every other currently fashionable ill. What these people fail to appreciate is that most law-abiding people will never even get a sniff of CS gas, and those who do get sprayed have generally asked for it. Usually, by the time the security forces have been graciously permitted to obtain a piece of equipment the criminal world has been thoroughly warned and (probably) instructed in how to evade it.

Leaving aside the tactical aspect and looking entirely towards the technical possibilities, what can we foresee?

Much of the equipment currently used by police and described in this book has 'trickled down' from technology developed for military purposes. Military contracts encourage advanced and expensive research and once the military application has been achieved the manufacturers look round for some other application. It is this which has produced night vision equipment, short range radar, perimeter protection systems and surveillance devices. So, one is inclined to ask what the military researchers are up to at the moment which might 'trickle down' into the police and security field. The most likely advances in the surveillance area seem to be the improvement and miniaturisation of thermal imaging equipment, and the possible application of millimetric-wave radar, which operates in a segment of the electro-magnetic spectrum bordering on the optical and thus the definition becomes much sharper than ordinary radar. We might, therefore, expect some advanced surveillance devices capable of operating in total darkness, dust, smoke and even through interfering screens; it might also prove useful in detection devices and as an EOD tool for examining a suspect article from a distance without having to place X-ray equipment alongside it.

The technology of mine-proof and explosion-proof vehicles is only beginning, and is another area which in the next decade might produce some practical results.

Military equipment advances in personal equipment, notably personal computers, will place a display upon the helmet visor and deliver orders, project maps and act as a weapon sight, being interconnected to the man's weapon. This may spin off into the security field, so that a police car or motorcyclist can have a map projected on his windscreen or visor directing him to an incident, or have the photograph of a wanted man projected for instant comparison. One must, though, beware of burdening the individual with too much electronic equipment and information.

Beyond this it seems unsafe to go. As this book shows, we are at a level of efficiency which will be satisfactory for years to come, and piling on new technology will not necessarily do the job more effectively. We must also bear in mind the constant factor of cost; to improve an existing system might very well produce a cost increase of 100 percent for an efficiency increase of only 10 percent. As with the military scene, the security scene is at a point where a startling breakthrough might be obtained, but at a startling price.

Right: Bombs are the common currency of terrorism, and countering them demands highly trained and dedicated experts with the best possible equipment and protection.

Above: Time spent on reconnaissance is seldom wasted and thermal imaging gives the ability to watch by day or night and penetrate camouflage.

Above: Is this the next generation of policeman? Countering terrorism means highly specialised equipment and forces.

Right: For situations where the risk is greatest, technology comes to the aid of the human being.

Weapons

Grenade launchers are intended to pitch a tear gas grenade into the middle of a rioting crowd or through a window in order to drive the occupants of the building out into the open where they can be rounded up. The earliest models were usually cups, mounted on the end of a single-barrel shotgun by means of a clamp, allowing standard hand grenades to be thrown with a moderate degree of accuracy to a moderate range - usually about 75 yards. But as rioters began getting more truculent; better organised and, particularly, better armed, it became imperative to have weapons with rather more range. In the 1960s and 1970s the US Army found itself getting more and more involved with riot control and, having a perfectly good grenade launching system in the 40 mm M79 and M203 weapons, asked for suitable tear gas grenades to be produced, so that they could avoid the need to have a separate and different weapon for riot work.

The M79/203 pattern weapon gives better accuracy and much longer range than the old-style cup discharger, but the price for the improved performance is a lesser payload; the 40 mm grenade carries much less CS composition than does the conventional canister-type hand grenade, though the answer to this was simply to fire more of them. There was also a slight tactical advantage in that the 40 mm grenade burned out rapidly and left little opportunity for heroes to pick them up and throw them back.

Once the grenade idea became public, it was rapidly picked up by commercial manufacturers who catered for police and other security forces, and now there are a number of launchers on the market, some still adhering to the old cup pattern, together with large grenades suited to their own particular launcher, others adopting the 40 mm standard but developing other launchers of a somewhat different pattern to the US military versions. The single-shot weapon has its adherents, but the small filling of the 40 mm grenade has led to further development of repeating weapons, with revolver-type cylinders, allowing a rapid barrage of gas to be built up and then 'stoked' regularly without demanding a number of weapons to produce the necessary quantity of ammunition on the target. Some countries have even gone as far as to produce long-range 40 mm riot control grenade rounds for use with automatic launchers, but this seems to be carrying things a little too far, and so far as we know, no police force has any intention of adopting such a weapon.

Riot Guns and **Shotguns:** Riot guns are a highly specialised class of firearms, built for no other purpose than to discharge 37 mm anti-riot grenades. They are single-shot, smoothbore guns, shoulder-arms or pistols, and they actually stem from the 37 mm flare pistols developed during World War Two for use as signalling devices by air forces. In the early stage of the development of anti-riot projectiles, pyrotechnic companies had the machinery for producing 37 mm cartridges and, for economy's sake, designed their anti-riot devices around this existing standard. As the cartridges became accepted throughout most of the world, so riot guns were designed around them and, as we have noted in the section on grenade launchers, there are even cases of weapons originally designed in 40 mm calibre used for military purposes being redesigned in 37 mm calibre in order to fire the available munitions.

But the riot gun is gradually losing ground; firstly the 40 mm grenade has begun to supplant the 37 mm riot cartridge as the preferred design. This is probably due to the same reason that saw the birth of the 37 mm riot grenades - because the 40 mm munition is in widespread use and manufacture, and with this existing production capacity it makes sense to adapt the anti-riot munitions to it. And on the other hand the past decade has seen considerable advances in the design of anti-riot cartridges used for the common 12-gauge shotgun, and a riot shotgun is probably as cheap as a pure riot gun and has greater versatility. Moreover, unlike riot guns and grenade launchers, the shotgun has, it is often felt, a more 'homely' appearance in the hands of police and does not have the 'police state' connotations that military-type weapons frequently suggest. This may well have been true when a double-barrelled sporting shotgun was occasionally seen in the hands of police, but it is a good deal less true of some of the high-technology shotguns currently on offer. The earliest approach to a specific 'police' shotgun came in the USA early in the century; from there it spread to the US Army as a trench-fighting weapon during World War One. This led to the arrival of a somewhat more sturdy model of pump-action shotgun with a shorter barrel than usual in the interests of handiness in trench raiding. This shorter and stronger design became the standard for US police and similar models were produced by the major manufacturers. Its adoption in European police forces did not become common until the 1960s. However, no sooner did European policemen begin adopting American pump shotguns, than the European shotgun makers began looking at the police market and producing some ideas of their own.

Automatic shotguns are generally accepted as being rather to fragile for the rough and tumble of police and military work, though they were used with some degree of success by the British Army in Malaya in the 1950s. But, again, the advance of modern technology has developed some sturdier designs, and certainly the selective - manual or automatic - shotgun has become a standard item in European forces, although the concept seems not to have attracted much interest in the USA.

Heckler & Koch MZP-1   Germany

The **MZP-1** single shot weapon first appeared as a 40 mm military grenade launcher, but once the military began showing more interest in automatic launchers, it was relaunched as a 37 mm police weapon, to fire any of the widely-available riot control grenades of this calibre. The 40 mm weapon is also still available for use with the newer 40 mm low-velocity grenades, and with these the range is considerably increased to about 350 metres. A simple and robust weapon, the barrel 'breaks' in the manner of a shotgun and a single cartridge can be loaded and the barrel swung back to lock to the breech. The striker then has to be hand-cocked, after which the manual safety can be applied if required. There is a fixed foresight and a large 'ladder' rear sight which lies along the top of the barrel when the weapon is carried, and is raised to a near-upright position for aiming. There is a telescoping stock, extended by simply grasping the butt, twisting and pulling.

Specification:

Calibre: 40 mm or 37 mm
Barrel length: 356 mm
Magazine: none: single shot
Length: stock folded: 463 mm
Length: stock extended: 683 mm
Weight, empty: 2.5 kg

Manufacturer:
Heckler & Koch, Oberndorf a/N, Germany

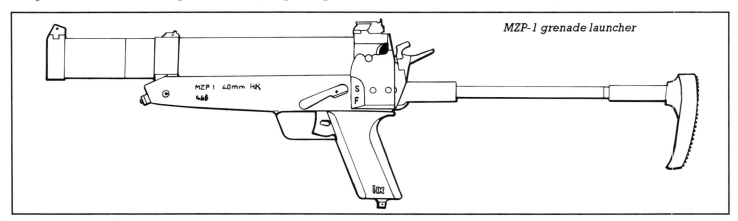

MZP-1 grenade launcher

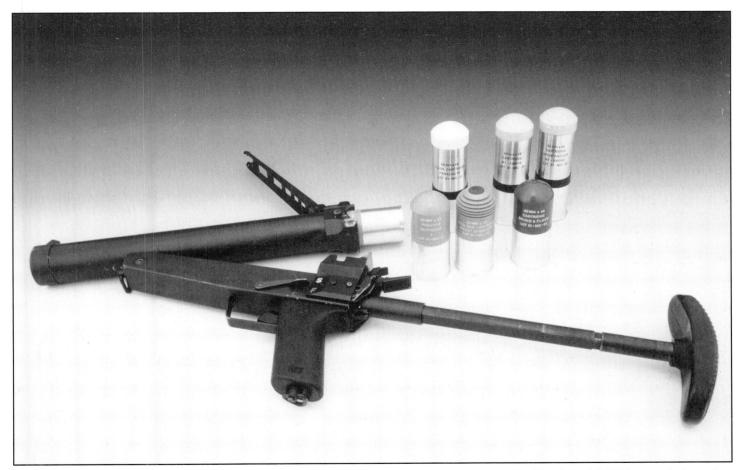

Heckler & Koch MZP-1 grenade launcher.

13

Dynamit Nobel

As an example of an older, single-shot, system which saw considerable use on the continent and is still in use in some places, the **Dynamit Nobel** 'RW' series of tear gas grenades can be studied. These were hand grenades in their basic form, but by simply screwing a light alloy pin on to the bottom of the grenade, the pin could then be thrust into the muzzle of any convenient rifle and launched by firing a special blank cartridge.

The grenade weighed 200 g and could go to a range of 80 metres, after which it would deliver a cloud of gas for some 20 seconds. A later, improved, model of this grenade had a styrofoam, streamlined cap fitted and was provided with a cup discharger which could be fitted to virtually any firearm, from signal pistols to shotguns, by means of a clamp and a range of adapters. Fired from a signal pistol the grenade would range to 70 metres, from a rifle to 120 metres.

Manufacturer:
Dynamit Nobel, Tromsdorf, Germany

Above right: *Dynamit Nobel launchers fitted to standard rifles.*
Below right: *Dynamit Nobel irritant smoke grenade.*

Specification:

Irritant Grenade RW702
Length: 96 mm
Diameter: 50 mm
Weight: 200 g
Agent: 15 g CS dust
Delay: 2-3 seconds
Emission time: 20 seconds
Range: 80 metres

Accuracy Systems M429 USA

There are times when the ability to send a stun grenade rather further than it can be thrown is an advantage, and the United States company **Accuracy Systems** developed their **M429** system in the late 1980s for just this occasion. Their **M429** stun grenade had been in production for some years, but in response to police requests the company then developed a cup discharger which couldbe adapted to fit most shotguns, riot guns and some revolvers. The **M429** grenade is a stun and flash grenade of cylindrical shape with the usual safety pin and fly-off lever firing mechanism. When the fuze functions, the flash and sound unit, which is made of cardboard so as not to produce any dangerous fragments, is ejected from the body of the grenade and explodes some distance away, another feature which ensures that the effect of the grenade is entirely psychological and without danger of producing serious injuries. To launch from a firearm, the grenade is loaded into the cup discharger with the lever held down by the wall of the cup; the

pin can then be withdrawn safely, and the grenade is launched by a blank cartridge. As the grenade leaves the cup, so the lever flies off and the fuze beings to burn, exploding the grenade after three to four seconds.

Accuracy Systems M429 launching system on revolver.

Manufacturer:
Accuracy Systems Inc., Phoenix, Ariz., USA

Specification:

No data released by the manufacturer

Hawk Engineering MM-1

This was probably the first revolver-type 40 mm grenade launcher, appearing from the USA in the late 1970s. A simple weapon, the **Hawk MM-1** uses a 12-chambered cylinder which is driven round by a spring, tensioned by the user during the process of loading the chambers. It will accept any type of 40 mm grenade, provided the length is not above 101 mm, thus preventing the use of the high-powered grenades intended for use in automatic launchers. A self-cocking firing mechanism allows a theoretical rate of fire of up to 144 rounds a minute, but 30 is generally accepted as a more realistic figure, and the maximum range is about 350 metres. Empty, it weighs 7.5 kg; loaded, with 12 grenades, the weight is over 10 kg, so this is not a lightweight weapon and not something one would wish to carry all day, but as a vehicle-carried reserve weapon for a riot squad, it has distinct advantages.

Manufacturer:
Hawk Engineering Inc., Lake Bluff, Illinois, USA

Specification:

Calibre: 40 mm
Length: 635 mm
Magazine: 12-shot cylinder
Weight, empty: 5.7 kg
Muzzle velocity: 76 m/s
Maximum range: 350 m
Practical rate of fire: 30 rds/min

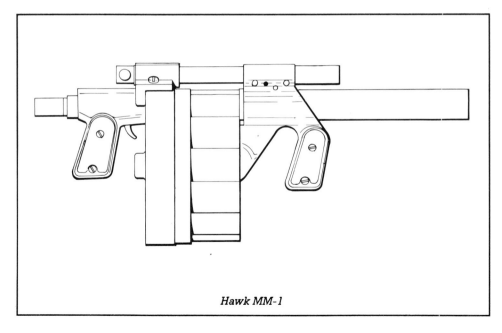

Hawk MM-1

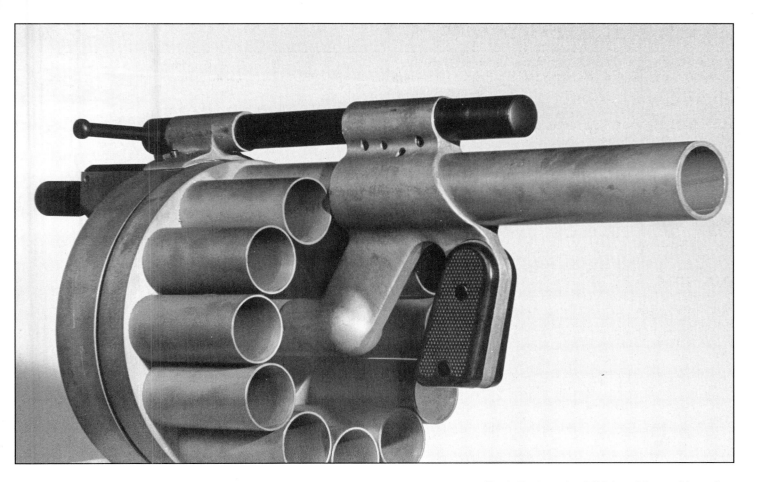

Hawk Engineering MM-1 multi-round launcher.

Mechem MGL

The **Mechem MGL** was developed in South Africa in the mid-1980s and might be said to represent the latest thinking on the revolver system of grenade launching. It was originally developed as a military weapon but it has since been extended to the security field and a range of anti-riot projectiles has been developed for this application. Loading is done by releasing the cylinder and swinging it out from the frame, where it can then be revolved to wind up a driving spring. The six chambers are then loaded with grenade cartridges and the cylinder locked back into the frame. On pressing the trigger the firing pin is first cocked and then released to fire the grenade. Gas pressure is then tapped from the barrel into a piston which unlocks the cylinder and allows the spring to turn it to align the next chamber, after which it locks once more, ready for the next shot. The sight is an 'occluded eye' sight with which the user aims with both eyes open. A red spot in the sight is superimposed on the user's view, and aiming is simply a matter of placing the red spot in the target. The sight has a rangefinding element built in and provides accurate aiming up to 375 metres range.

Specification:

Calibre: 40 mm
Barrel length: 356 mm
Magazine: none: single shot
Length: stock folded: 566 mm
Length: stock extended:788 mm

Weight, empty: 5.3 kg
Muzzle velocity: 76 m/s
Maximum range: 350 m
Manufacturer:
Mechem, Silverton, South Africa

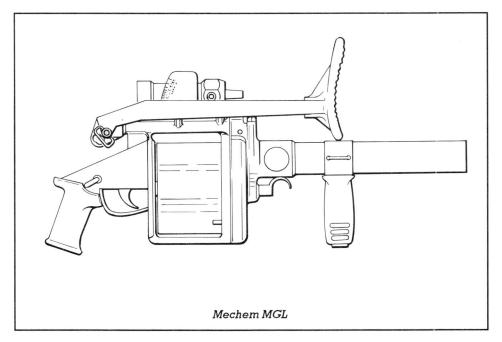

Mechem MGL

Mechem MGL as made under licence in Portugal.

Schermuly Riot Gun

This is known as a 'multi-purpose' gun since it can be adapted to a variety of roles, making it a highly cost-effective weapon. The basic weapon is a smoothbore 38 mm single-shot gun which breaks open, like a shotgun, for loading and is fired by a self-cocking mechanism which, when the trigger is pulled, first cocks and then releases the firing pin. An adapter barrel can be fitted into the 38 mm barrel to permit the firing of smaller 12-gauge shotgun ammunition; this adapter barrel can be smoothbored or rifled, to permit firing slugs. A cup discharger can be fitted to the muzzle to allow the firing of large tear gas grenades The wooden butt, adjustable front hand grip and adjustable sights make this an accurate and comfortable weapon to fire.

Specification:

Magazine: none: single shot
Length overall: 820 mm
Weight: 2.7 kg
Sight range: 50/100/150 m

Manufacturer:
Pains-Wessex Schermuly, High Post, Salisbury, Wiltshire, England

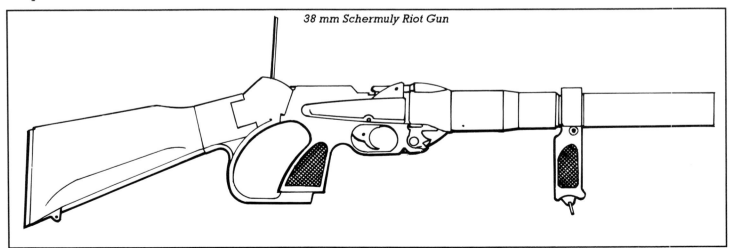

38 mm Schermuly Riot Gun

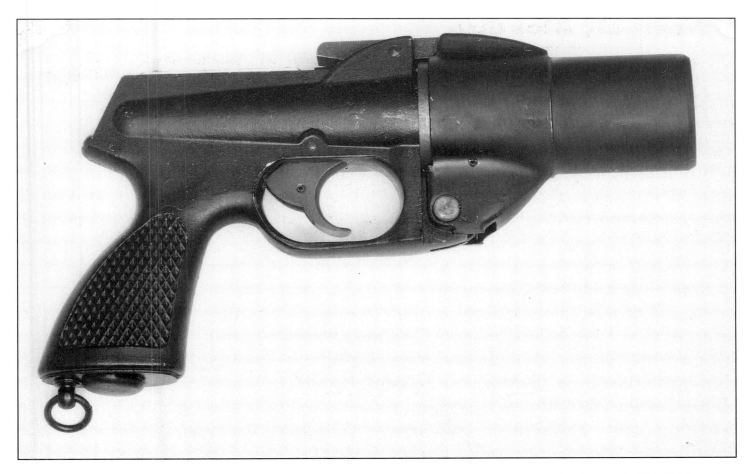

The Schermuly Riot Pistol version.

Federal M203A Riot Gun   USA

This is a simple, smoothbore, single-shot weapon which has been in production for many years and is widely used throughout the world. It fires the standard 37/38 mm type of riot cartridge, and can also be fitted with a special cup on the muzzle to permit firing Federal Laboratories tear gas grenades. Operation is very easy; pressing on a thumb-catch releases the barrel to swing down, exposing the chamber for loading. Then the cartridge is loaded, the gun closed, the hammer manually cocked and the trigger pressed to fire; alternatively the trigger can be pulled through in double-action mode to cock and fire. The forward grip can be adjusted slightly to suit the owner's fancy, but beyond that there is nothing to adjust and nothing very much to get out of order. The gun is 27.75 inches long and weighs 3.7 lbs.

Federal Laboratories have recently been taken over by Mace Security of Bennington, Vermont, but are still functioning as the Federal Labs division of Mace.

Specification:

Calibre: 38 mm
Length overall: 737 mm
Weight, empty: 2.58 kg
Operation: double action

Manufacturer: Federal Laboratories, Saltsburg, Penn., USA

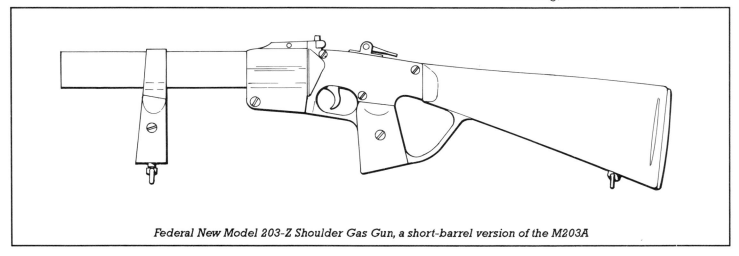

Federal New Model 203-Z Shoulder Gas Gun, a short-barrel version of the M203A

Federal M203A Riot Gun with carrying case.

23

Winchester Defender Shotgun

The **Model 1300 Defender** is a conventional slide-action 12-gauge shotgun chambered for 3 inch cartridges. The breech is closed by a chrome-molybdenum steel rotating bolt with four locking lugs, and unlocking is recoil-assisted, giving a very fast reloading cycle. Although to the same general design as a sporting shotgun, the **Defender** is heavier and more robustly constructed so as to stand up to the rough-and-tumble of police and military work. There is also a version made in stainless steel for use in marine applications where seawater corrosion is a permanent hazard.

Manufacturer:
U.S. Repeating Arms Co., New Haven, Conn. USA

Specification:

Cartridge: 12-ga, 70 or 76 mm
Barrel length: 457 mm
Magazine: 6-shot tubular plus one in chamber
Length: 1032 mm
Weight, empty: 3.17 kg

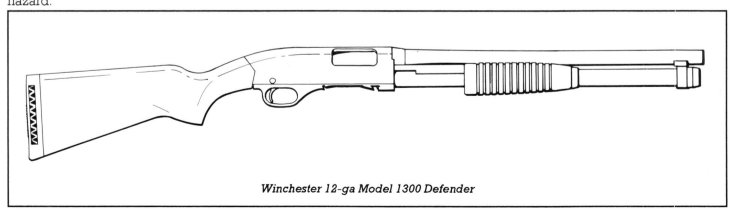

Winchester 12-ga Model 1300 Defender

Beretta M3P Shotgun   Italy

The **Beretta M3P** shotgun is a 'Dual-Functioning Model' (DFM) 12-gauge shotgun capable of semi-automatic or slide action sat the firer's choice. The semi-automatic action allows rapid fire, while the slide action permits the use of specialised ammunition or grenade launching attachments. The change from one function to the other is done by simply turning a ring set in the front of the fore-end, where it can easily be operated by the supporting hand. The semi-automatic action relies upon recoil, an inertia locking system holding the rotating bolt closed. Operating the change switch shifts the operation of the inertia block to the slide mechanism. Feed is from a 5-shot box magazine, and the butt can be folded forward, over the top of the receiver, and locked in that position to form a useful carrying handle.

Specification:

Cartridge: 12-ga, 70 mm
Barrel length: 610 mm
Magazine: 5-shot box
Length: stock folded: 940 mm
Length: stock extended: 1150 mm
Weight, empty: 3.54 kg

Manufacturer:
P. Beretta SpA, Gardone val Trompia, Italy

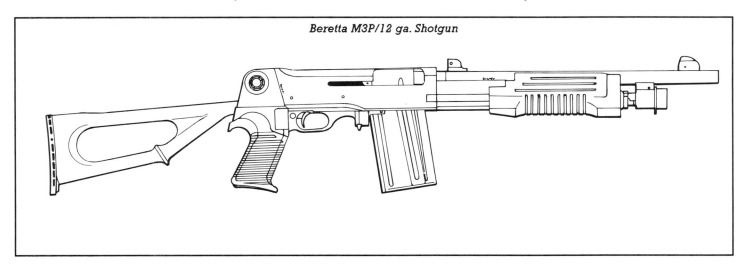

Beretta M3P/12 ga. Shotgun

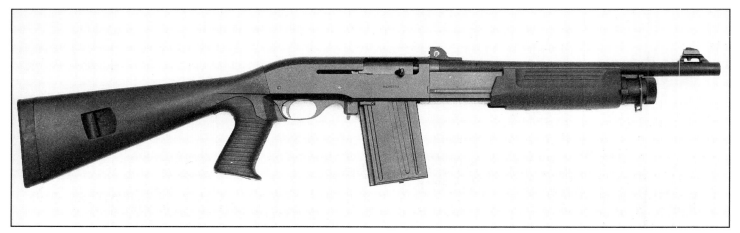

Above: Beretta M3P with fixed stock and pistol grip.   *Below:* Beretta M3T long barrel model with stock folded.

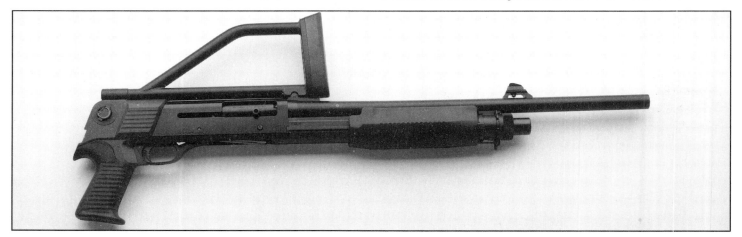

Beretta M3P with stock folded to form carrying handle.

Franchi SPAS-12   Italy

The **SPAS** (Special Purpose Automatic Shotgun) was the first of the 'purpose-built' shotguns designed for police and security use and it attained a considerable popularity after its introduction in 1979. The gun is a short-barrelled 12-gauge semi-automatic with a folding butt which has a special attachment to allow the user to carry and operate the weapon one-handed. The receiver is of light alloy, and the barrel and gas cylinder are chrome-plated to prevent corrosion. The tubular magazine beneath the barrel carries 7 rounds, and the semi-automatic action will fire 4 rounds per second. Pressing a button in the fore-end will convert the action from semi-automatic to manual slide action,

the fore-end becoming the operating slide. This system is provided so that lightweight ammunition such as tear gas grenades and rubber shot can be fired; these have too light a projectile to allow the gas-driven semi-automatic action to function reliably. A grenade launcher can also be fitted when the gun is used in the manual mode. The butt has a hooklike piece on the rear end which, when the pistol grip is being held and with the gun at waist-level, hooks beneath the firer's elbow and allows his one arm to take the weight of the gun, a useful feature when the other arm is occupied with holding a prisoner or for firing out of a vehicle window.

Specification:

Cartridge: 12-ga, 70 mm
Barrel length: 460 mm
Magazine: 7-shot tubular plus one in chamber
Length: stock folded: 710 mm
Length: stock extended: 930 mm
Weight, empty: 4.0 kg

Manufacturer:
Luigi Franchi SpA, Fornaci, Italy

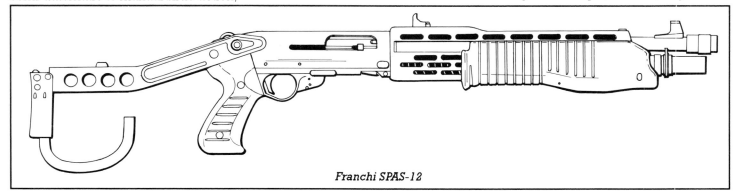

Franchi SPAS-12

28

Franchi SPAS-15   Italy

After the success of the **SPAS-12** Franchi conferred with various police and security forces who were using the weapon and then set about developing an improved model which would use a box magazine instead of the tubular magazine. This resulted in the SPAS-14 which, while workable, had a number of shortcomings and never went into production. Instead, the design team sat down with a clean sheet of paper and came up with an entirely fresh design, the **SPAS-15**, which went into production in 1988.

As with the SPAS-12, the **SPAS-15** is a dual-function weapon, providing either gas-actuated semi-automatic fire or manual slide action. The ammunition feeds from a box magazine, and after the last shot in the magazine has been fired the action remains open, with the bolt back, to close automatically when a fresh magazine is inserted, loading the top round as it does so. Slide or semi-automatic action is selected by a button in the fore-end, as with the SPAS-12. The receiver and barrel are of steel, and the barrel can be fitted with a grenade launcher cup or with a 'shot diverter', a special attachment which gives a charge of shot a much faster spread at short ranges, which is particularly useful when firing inside a building.

The tubular butt folds to the side of the receiver, and there is a permanent carrying handle on top of the receiver, protecting the cocking handle (used only when initially cocking for semi-automatic action). This carrying handle also acts as a sight bracket and can be used to mount night sights or other aiming devices.

Specification:

Cartridge: 12-ga, 70 mm
Barrel length: 406 mm
Magazine: 6-shot box .
Length: stock folded: 700 mm
Length: stock extended: 915 mm
Weight, empty: 3.9 kg

Manufacturer:
Luigi Franchi SpA, Fornaci, Italy

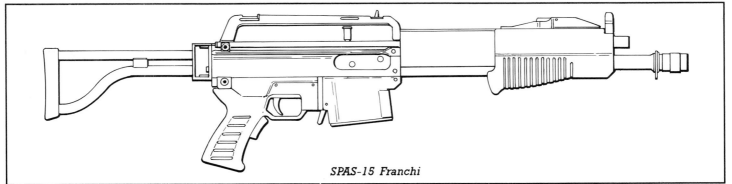

SPAS-15 Franchi

Layout of Franchi-15 showing all options available for specific occasions.

Denel Striker

The **Striker** was developed in South Africa and has appeared under various names in different countries, and appears to have been licensed to a number of firms at one time or another. It was designed as a military, police and anti-terrorist weapon, and fires 12-gauge cartridges by means of a 12-shot cylinder. This is gate-loaded, in the manner of an old-fashioned revolver pistol; a gate at the right rear of the cylinder is opened, exposing a chamber. A cartridge is loaded and then a slight pressure on the trigger indexes the cylinder round one notch to bring another empty chamber into place for loading. This is repeated until the cylinder is full. Unloading of the empty cases is done in a similar manner,

pushing back on a fixed ejected rod to the lower right side of the barrel so as to eject the empty case through the gate before loading a fresh cartridge.

Once the cylinder has been loaded, a key on the front is turned to tension a driving spring. On pulling the trigger the firing pin is first cocked and then released, firing the cartridge, and as the trigger is pulled a second time so the spring drives the cylinder round to align the next cartridge. The barrel is cylinder-bored so that solid slugs can be fired. A metal stock folds over the top of the receiver, and there is a front grip, so that it can be fired from the hip in sub-machine gun fashion or from the shoulder.

Specification:

Cartridge: 12-ga, 70 mm
Barrel length: 300 mm
Magazine: 12-shot cylinder
Length: stock folded: 500 mm
Length: stock extended: 780 mm
Weight, empty: 4.2 kg

Manufacturer:
Denel (Pty) Ltd,
Hennopsmere, South Africa

Below left: Standard Striker with folded stock.
Below right: Striker with long barrel and stock extended.

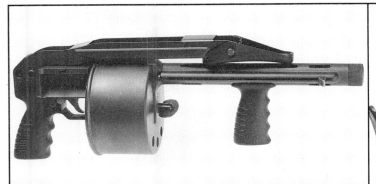

Knight Master Key S

USA

The **'Master Key S'** is a shotgun/rifle combination more or less based upon the well-known M203 40 mm grenade launcher. It fits underneath an M16 or AR15 automatic carbine in the same way, but instead of launching a grenade it fires a standard 12-gauge 70 mm cartridge. Hence the name **'Master Key'**, because a well-placed 12-gauge shot charge will open most doors. The shotgun unit is a highly-modified Remington Model 870; the butt is removed and the barrel and magazine shortened, but sufficient length is left to permit the slide action to work properly. The unit is positioned beneath the carbine's barrel, using the bayonet lug as a locating point, by means of mounting brackets welded to the shotgun unit, and the carbine magazine makes a convenient handgrip, the trigger being just ahead of it.

The carbine works in the normal way; no modification being necessary. If preferred, for a particular task, the shotgun unit can be removed and fitted with a pistol grip so that it can be operated as a separate weapon, and, of course, the two can be parted to permit the carbine to be used separately at any time. There is, though, little point in this, since the combination is relatively light, of convenient size, and not cumbersome in use.

Specification:

No data released by the manufacturer

Manufacturer:

Knight's Armament Co., Vero Beach, Florida, USA

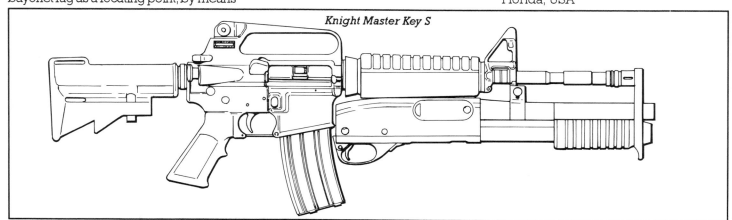

Knight Master Key S

Ciener 'Ultimate' Combination USA

The **Ciener 'Ultimate'** is much the same sort of weapon as the Knight 'Master Key S' and, in fact, was the first such combination to appear, in the early 1980s. The shotgun unit in this case is mounted beneath the standard M16/AR15 rifle, rather than the carbine version, and the basic weapon is the same, shortened Remington Model 870 12-gauge shotgun. Fixing is done by a clip mounting which attaches to the bayonet boss and a yoke mounting which is fitted to the rifle receiver and accepts the rear end of the shotgun unit. The shotgun stock is removed and the trigger is close to the rifle magazine, so that the magazine can be used as the handgrip when firing the shotgun. A replacement upper receiver unit is provided for the rifle, which incorporates the yoke fitting to accept the shotgun. The shotgun is simply pushed into the yoke and the bayonet lug fitting is sprung over the lug; pressure on two spring clips releases the unit instantly. The special upper receiver makes no difference to the operation of the rifle, and if the shotgun is removed there is no pressing need to change the upper receiver again since the yoke does not interfere with operation.

Specification:
No data released by the manufacturer

Manufacturer:
J.A. Ciener Inc., Cape Canaveral, Florida, USA

The Ciener 'Ultimate' combination gun..

Weapon Sights and Aiming Aids

The use of firearms by police and security forces is not the same as their use by military forces. The object of military firepower is to smother the enemy with fire so that he cannot use his own weapons effectively. As a British statesman once said, "It is not a question of hitting a particular button on the enemy's coat, rather of driving home effective fire into his body of infantry". He was speaking in the flintlock era, but his observation is still valid for the general run of battle. Police and security forces, on the other hand, use fire power as a surgical tool, to incapacitate hostage-takers, hijackers, riot leaders and similar key figures in the opposition, and they therefore tend to be more likely to use sophisticated sighting equipment. Sighting telescopes are commonplace; night vision sights are becoming more common, and particularly the image intensifying sight - thermal imaging sights are not yet small enough nor cheap enough for police forces. Other aids to sighting in common use are the various forms of laser spotlight,

either visible or infra-red. Opinions on the utility of the visible spot are mixed; more than one police officer has observed that if the laser is aimed at one individual in a group, the others take it as a sign that they are not targeted and are thus more likely to try a sudden move. The infra-red spot, used in conjunction with night vision goggles, is therefore a preferred method of assisting a fast aim.

A system which, after many years of trying, is becoming better known and more used is the collimating sight, or occluded eye sight, a device which allows the firer to keep both eyes open while aiming and thus give him a wider field of view so that he can see what is going on around his target. These sights display a dot or ring or some other marker which, due to the use of both eyes, appears to be projected out to the target. By simply laying the marker on the target, the sighting is completed. It makes no difference where the firer puts his eye or head; provided he can see the marker on the target, the weapon is correctly aimed, and

there are no parallax problems to worry about. For quick and accurate shooting, this type of sight is in a class of its own.

One of the problems with a sniper waiting his opportunity to deal with, say, a hostage-holder, is that a very great deal depends upon his judgment, because he, with his telescope, is the only one who can see precisely what is going on. Because of this, and because the sniper may not be in full possession of relevant information, a new tendency is to wire his sighting telescope into a video circuit so that what he is watching can be seen by his controllers, who can also speak directly to him by radio or wire. Not all police officers are entirely in agreement with this; there is always a tendency, they claim, for a committee meeting to assemble in front of the screen and debate the issue while the opportunity the sniper awaits comes and goes without a shot being fired. It remains to be seen whether these systems of sniper control find a following.

All sorts of people use advanced sights; an Afghan guerrilla takes aim with a Russian Dragunov sniping rifle fitted with the PSO-1 telescope sight.

MALOS Sight

Israel

MALOS stands for 'Miniature Laser Optical Sight' and comprises a laser rangefinder, a sighting telescope and a ballistic computer in one unit. Slightly larger than a conventional telescope sight, it can be mounted on any type of weapon. The computer needs to be programmed for the particular weapon and ammunition combination being used, and also has manual controls for windage and elevation which permit adjustment for the wind, for bore-sighting (zeroing) and for use in emergency should the electronic systems fail.

To use the sight, the firer takes aim at his target and presses a switch, which can be mounted at any convenient place on the weapon. The laser rangefinder takes the range and passes it to the computer, which then calculates the elevation and drift and adjusts the sighting marker in the telescope. The firer now takes aim again, using the new marker, and fires. Under normal conditions he should hit; if there is a strong wind, then he is expected to compensate by using the manual controls.

MALOS is robust and designed to withstand the rough and tumble of everyday use, within sensible limits.

Manufacturer: ELOP Electro-Optical Industries, Rehovot, Israel

The MALOS sight fitted to the Israeli Galil rifle.

Signaal UA 1137/UA 1116 Sights Netherlands

The **Signaal UA 1116 II** sight is a second-generation image-intensifier sight specifically designed for military small arms and machine guns; it fits the NATO-standard STANAG 2324 sight mounting bracket. The weight has been kept as low as possible consistent with the desired reliability and ruggedness. Optical magnification is 4.2X and it is capable of picking up targets at normal firing ranges in starlight; for the technically-minded, the resolution is 1 milli-radian at a light level of 1 milli-lux. The sight weighs 1.6 kg and is powered by 3 volts, delivered by various types of battery.

Manufacturer: Signaal-USFA, Eindhoven, the Netherlands

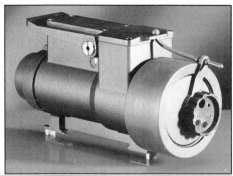

The **Signaal UA 1137** is an unusual type of night sight in that it does not require batteries. It is self-powered from a generator operated by a noiseless lever on top of the sight. A single push of this lever generates enough electricity to keep the sight operating for a length of time more than sufficient to detect a target, take aim and fire. Since there are no batteries to insert, there is no need to open up the sight, and the entire unit is sealed and waterproof; it can be put on the shelf for five years without needing to be periodically tested.

The unit is a second-generation image intensifier with an optical magnification of 1.5X; it has been carefully designed to give a 22° wide field of view but only 10° vertical field, so that the firer's view is shielded from the open sky above and from his own muzzle flash below. It weighs less than 1.5 kg, and apart from keeping the lenses clean, requires no maintenance.

Top Centre: The Signaal UA 1137 self-powered sight.

Left: The Signaal UA 1116 image-intensifying sight.

Teleranger Sight   Germany

The **Teleranger** was developed by an Austrian company called Optik-Elektronik but has since been taken up by the well-known Mauser company. It is a specially compact laser rangefinder which can be attached to almost any type of optical or electro-optical sight to provide an instant and accurate range for setting on the sight. Optik-Elektronik originally intended to incorporate a rangefinder, telescope and ballistic computer into a single unit, but then decided that people who had already invested large sums of money in sights might prefer to have an add-on device rather then buy a complete new sight unit.

The **Teleranger** is a neat oblong box which clamps to the sight; it can measure ranges from 70 to 2000 metres with an accuracy of 5 metres, and displays the result on a red LED display alongside the eyepiece of the associated sight. This display has automatic brightness control, so that it shines more brightly in daylight, for easy visibility, but glows gently in the dark so as not to dazzle the firer or give his location away. Measuring 290 mm long and weighing 1.3 kg, the unit is powered by six AA batteries.

Manufacturer: Mauserwerke, Oberndorf, Germany

The Mauser Teleranger sight mounted above the sighting telescope on the Mauser 86SR sniping rifle.

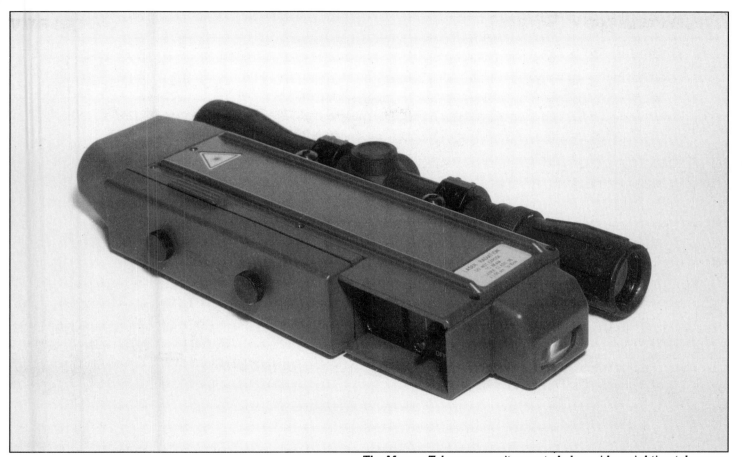

The Mauser Teleranger unit mounted alongside a sighting telescope.

Sopelem TN2-1 France

The **TN2-1** is actually a night vision goggle, described as a night observation and driving aid, but when used in combination with the Sopelem PS1 or PS2 spotlight projector, it becomes a very efficient aiming aid. The spotlight delivers a precise laser beam in the infra-red spectrum, invisible to the naked eye. It can be fitted to almost any firearm and zeroed to coincide with the axis of the weapon's barrel. A simple push-button switch can be mounted in any convenient place on the weapon to control the light. The firer then puts on the night vision goggles, enabling him to see the infra-red spot, and takes aim with the rifle. In this case, 'taking aim' does not mean looking over or through the sights; the firer simply points the rifle until the laser spot is on the target, and then presses the trigger. He can be holding it in any convenient manner - at the hip, tucked under his arm or resting on a wall, it doesn't matter. So long as spot and target coincide, and he can see this in his night goggles, the shot will strike where the spot is. Provided, of course, that he has carefully zeroed the spot to the rifle.

A French soldier using the Sopelem TN2-1 goggles with the PS-1 laser spot fitted to his FAMAS rifle.

Manufacturer: Sopelem-Sofretec, Bezons, France

Aimpoint 1000 Sweden

This is an example of the collimating sight referred to on page 34; the eyepiece of this sight is intended to be viewed by one eye while the other eye can be open or closed - preferably open, so that the field of view covers more than could be seen through a conventional telescope sight. The electro-optical system causes a red spot to appear in the field of view at the point of aim of the weapon, and all the firer needs to do is move the weapon so that the red spot is superimposed upon his selected target. The positioning of the dot is entirely dependent upon the movement of the weapon and is not affected by movement of the firer's head. It can be used in any and all weather conditions, does not advertise its presence to the enemy, and the technique of using it effectively is rapidly learned.

The **Aimpoint 1000** is a simple and rugged piece of equipment which is designed to fit the well-known Weaver sight base; there is also an Aimpoint 2000 which is designed to fit into standard one-inch telescope rings and which can be fitted with a 3X telescope add-on unit which enlarges the field of view seen by the sighting eye, thus increasing the range at which accurate shooting can be done.

Above right: *The Aimpoint 1000 rifle sight.*
Below right: *An Aimpoint 1000 sight fitted to the M16 rifle, indicating its small size.*

Manufacturer:
Aimpoint AB, Malmo, Sweden

AIM-1/D Aiming Light

Israel

This is another laser aiming spot, similar to the Sopelem PS-1 and PS2 devices described above. It can be fitted to any weapon from a pistol upwards, and there are a number of accessories which permit varying the light intensity and operating it by remote control. The beam diverges at an angle of 0.3 milliradians (about one minute of arc), so that at 100 yards range it will project a spot of infra-red light about one and a half inches across, which is certainly small enough to make a precise aiming mark. The maximum beam power is about 2 milliwatts, and the unit can run from 10 to 50 hours on a couple of AA batteries, depending upon what sort of battery and whether the unit is using low, high or intermediate power. There is also a more powerful version generating 20 milliwatts which can project its beam up to 3 km distance. This is intended for heavy machine guns, recoilless rifles and similar crew-served weapons, but it could also have its uses as an infra-red spotlight or marker for surveillance purposes, since at that range the beam spot is about one metre in diameter.

Manufacturer:
International Technologies , (Lasers), Rishon, Letzion, Israel

The AIM-1/D laser spot fitted to an M16 rifle.

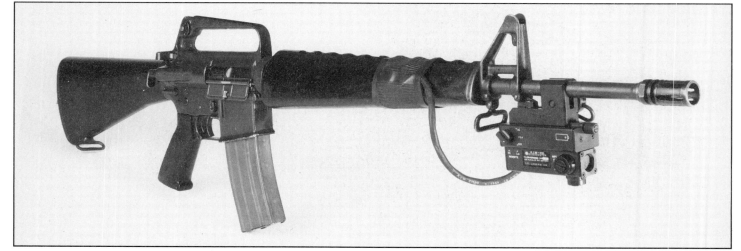

The AIM-1/D laser unit in use with the Litton M972 night vision goggles.

Sure-Fire Light/laser Systems

The **Sure-Fire light system** is an exceptionally compact spotlight which uses a 3 or 6 watt high pressure xenon lamp system powered by lithium batteries. This produces a powerful beam of white light, zeroed to the weapon, which can be used to identify and engage targets to a range in excess of 50 metres. Filters can be placed over the projection lens to convert the output to the infra-red spectrum, so rendering the beam invisible to the naked eye and allowing it to be used with night vision equipment.

The **Sure-Fire laser system** is similar but uses a 5 milliwatt laser diode which can be either red or infra-red. These produce an intense red spot which can be seen on buildings out to several hundred metres at night and which can also be used indoors in daylight, giving a visible light at close-quarter ranges.

These systems are provided in two forms. The **Sure-Fire 1 system** is modular, small, and can be fitted with either the light system or the laser system. Either can be interchanged in the field without the use of tools, so that the system can be changed to suit the operating conditions in a few minutes. If necessary, both units can be fitted together, though this cannot be done on pistols. **The Sure-Fire 2 system**

combines both light and laser in a single integrated unit, and can be switched to 'light only' or 'light plus laser' operation. It is smaller than the combined use of both systems on **Sure-Fire 1** and can thus be used on pistols. A wide variety of mountings to fit either system to most types of weapon in common use are available.

Manufacturer:
Laser Products, Fountain Valley, Calif. USA

Sure-Fire 2 combined xenon lamp and laser spot fitted to a Beretta 92 pistol.

Elbit SC3 Sniper Control System   Israel

The **Elbit SC3 system** is designed to co-ordinate and control the operations of a group of up to five snipers by means of line or radio transmission of each sniper's telescope image to a central point. By continuous video transmission of these sight pictures, the commander has total knowledge and control of the situation, allowing him to command hostage rescue and SWAT teams to take decisive action while minimising the risk to hostages and security personnel.

The sight images are captured by means of a unique miniaturised video camera which fits into the sighting telescope. There is no need for line-of-sight adjustment when fitting it, and the sniper's ability to adjust his sight for focus is not affected. The unit can be fitted or removed in half a minute.

The system can use a radio link to a range of about 5 km in open country and about 850 metres in built-up areas. Alternatively, a transmission line of 150 metres length is provided for each camera, and this can be increased if necessary. The pictures are displayed to the commander on 4 inch screens.

Manufacturer:
Elbit Computers, Haifa, Israel

The Elbit SC3 sniper control system, showing the various controller's monitors and the telescope sights fitted with miniature video cameras.

45

Simrad KN250   Norway

One of the drawbacks with using electronic sights at night and ordinary optical sights by day is that the sights have to be changed at dusk and dawn. Mechanically a simple task, but the question of whether both sights are optically zeroed with the rifle is not quite so easy. The **Simrad KN250** night sight solves this problem; the day telescope sight is left on the rifle, and the night sight is clamped on top of it when required. Instead of an eyepiece, the image intensifier unit has a folded optical path which ends in a prism in front of the telescope's object lens. The telescope sight remains zeroed to the rifle, while the night sight position is not critical; no boresighting adjustment is required, so it can easily be fitted in a few seconds. The optical telescope can be used until dusk; the masking cover at the front of the prism is then flipped up and the night sight switched on. On looking through the telescope the firer sees his usual telescope graticule superimposed upon the green image intensifier picture of the scene in front of him, and he can take aim in confidence that the rifle is going to hit what

the cross-wires are aligned upon. The **KN250** weighs 740 grammes, including its two AA batteries; the magnification, of course, depends entirely upon the optical sight, the **KN250** merely reproducing what it sees there.

Manufacturer:
Simrad Optronics A/S, Oslo, Norway

The Simrad KN250 night vision sight attached to a standard optical telescope sight, giving day or night use.

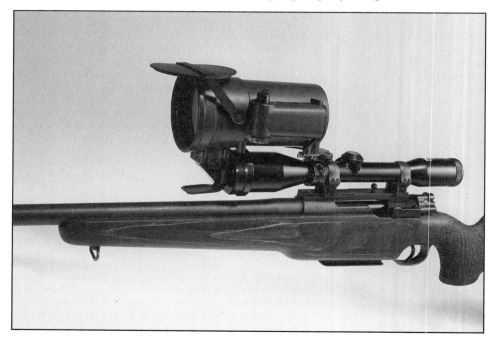

Imatronic LS45

The **LS45** is an eyesafe laser projector which directs an intense red spot of light on to the target. There is no need to bring the weapon to the shoulder; it can be fired from the hip or any other convenient manner, and thus can often allow a shot to be fired without alerting the target by adopting the usual weapon-at-the-shoulder firing position. The beam diameter is only 0.34 mm and it projects a spot of 24 cm diameter at 100 metres range. The beam is sufficiently powerful to operate at ranges in excess of 500 metres. The system can be used with any weapon capable of using standard dovetail telescope mounts; elevation and windage adjustments are provided, and there is also an iron sight built into the casing for emergency use.

Manufacturer:
Imatronic, Wokingham, Berks. England

Below left: The Imatronic LS45 sight on an Uzi submachine gun.

Below right: Showing the versatility of the Imatronic sight, the LS45 unit on a police shotgun.

N/SEAS Single Eye Acquisition Sight   Israel

This is a night vision goggle allied to a laser spotlight, but unlike the usual night vision goggle it only requires the use of one eye, and the wearer can select which eye he chooses to use with the night vision viewer and which he prefers to use naked. He can thus leave his master eye naked and use it to fire a rifle by means of a night vision sight mounted on the rifle, and at the same time he has his other eye with the ability to view the scene in darkness and also shoot his rifle by means of the laser spot, if this is preferable. Alternatively the unit can be removed from the head harness or face mask and fitted directly to a rifle, as seen here, and used in conjunction with the laser spot projector. The viewer uses a 2nd or 3rd generation micro-amplifier, has a field of view of 40° and weighs only 415 grammes.

Manufacturer:
International Technologies (Lasers), Rishon Letzion, Israel

Below left: *The N/SEAS single eye sight fitted to a head harness.*

Below right: *The N/SEAS single eye sight removed from the head harness and used as a rifle sight, together with its associated laser spot projector.*

Magnavox SRTS

The **Magnavox SRTS** (Short Range Thermal Sight) is one of the first of this type of sight, developed in the late 1980s and still being worked on. It is an infra-red imaging sight developed for the US Army and is included here simply as an example, since it is not yet available for service.

The sight is entirely self-contained and driven by a standard military lithium battery. Infra-red energy from the scene being viewed is collected by the lens, after which it is scanned by an oscillating mirror and then focused on to 63 lead selenide detector elements which convert the infra-red energy into electronic signals. The output of each detector is fed to a high-gain amplifier and these outputs are then merged into a single video signal. This goes to a miniature cathode ray tube where other signals controlling the sighting graticule are also inserted, and the final result is viewed through an optical eyepiece. There are a few simple controls and the extensive use of modular components makes the sight quite robust and easy to maintain and service.

The model shown here, one of the earliest designs, weighed just over 1.8 kg and was 300 mm long, 86 mm wide and 102 mm deep. It had a field of view 6° wide and 4° high and could operate for ten hours on one battery. The US Army have now undertaken full-scale engineering development of the design.

Manufacturer:
Magnavox Electro-Optical Systems, Mahwah, NJ, USA

The Magnavox SRTS infra-red sight on an M16 rifle.

Access Control and Perimeter Protection

Access Control and **Perimeter Protection** are, really, two sides of the same coin. **Access Control** is the business of allowing only authorised people to enter an area, while **Perimeter Protection** is the business of keeping unauthorised people out. As you might expect there is, therefore, a certain amount of overlap between the two functions, and a system designed for one will probably do a certain amount of the other.

Access Control systems usually rely upon some form of identification of the individual being presented; commonly, a magnetic-stripe card is used, since it is cheap, easily understandable, and if used in conjunction with a Personal Identity Number (PIN) gives a very good degree of security. Moreover, most people are familiar with the card/PIN concept from using bank cards and credit cards, so there is no technology barrier to be overcome by the personnel. But card/PIN systems are far from foolproof, because there are still people who write their PIN on a piece of paper and keep it in their wallet or purse alongside the card.

And thus, for establishments demanding a higher degree of security, biometric systems have been developed. There are fingerprint readers, readers which study the retina of the eyeball (which is, apparently, as individual as a fingerprint), and readers which actually study the face of the applicant and compare it with a photograph stored in the system memory. Add one or more of these to a card/PIN system and you begin to have something which is very secure. The only trouble is that it becomes something of an annoyance to the staff, who then spend most of their waking hours trying to invent something which will fool the system; not for any criminal purpose, merely to get their own back.

Whatever the system, it has to have some features built in which might not be obvious at first glance. For example, the system must prevent one man opening the door with his card/PIN combination and then having half-a-dozen others come in after him without having shown their cards. It must also keep track of who goes in and out; having once admitted Mr., Brown 4637, the system must then prevent a second Mr Brown 4637 from coming in until the first has gone out. It should also be capable of sorting out who is admitted where; truck-drivers have no need to gain access to the research laboratory or the accountant's office, so their card must be recognised by a reader for those departments and access refused. The system should also keep a log of movements, so that should some incident occur, then the people in that area at the time can be instantly identified by the control system. This is far from being an exhaustive list, but it will at least indicate that there is more to access control than having a uniformed doorman.

Perimeter Protection is generally more brusque; its job is simply to keep the evildoers out and provide as few entrances as possible for the authorised, with rigorous access control at those points. The simple answer is a chain-link fence topped with barbed wire; the complicated answer is a computer-controlled video system backed up by machine guns. This scans the surrounding area and constantly compares the picture with a stored picture of the same area with nobody in it. If a figure suddenly appears the system alerts an operator who can then demand, through a loudspeaking system, the identity of the intruder. If no answer, or the wrong answer, is forthcoming, he fires a machine gun which is mounted on the same platform as the video camera and zeroed to the camera's field of view. This may sound drastic, but it is certainly in use on some Middle Eastern oil rigs.

In between these two extremes there is a wide variety of systems which can detect the presence of an intruder. Some sound an alarm which will scare him off, others alert an operator who can organise a reception party. Most systems are partitioned so that the point of entry is rapidly identified in order to guide security staff to it quickly. Some systems allow the intruder to get inside and then retaliate; one, for example, waits until he is inside the building and then fills it with tear gas and smoke so that he cannot find his way out. Some are obvious - barbed wire - others are not - radar or infra-red beams. Unlike access control systems, perimeter protection systems rarely need to keep checks on people, but they do need to have some safeguards so that they do not react to birds and animals native to the area, or to extremes of climate, otherwise the false alarm rate can become a burden.

The most obvious boundary barrier to a site is a fence, usually a strong chain-link with a few strands of barbed or razor wire on the top. But fences can be scaled or cut, and the most common form of protection to be added to such a fence is a simple motion detector. The fence is carefully tensioned between its supports, motion detectors are fitted to each section and wired to a central control point, and any abnormal disturbance of the fence, as for example, throwing a ladder across it, will sound the alarm and indicate which section of the fence is under threat. An argument against this system is that a careful cutting of the fence could, conceivably, evade the motion detectors, although if the fence is correctly tensioned the act of cutting will be sufficient to release some of the tension and sound the alarm. However, to cater for the cutter, a fibre-optic cable can be inconspicuously woven into the fence wire; cutting this, or placing it under strain, interferes with a pulsed signal constantly passing through it and sounds the alarm. Again, it is possible to identify the point of attack quite closely when using this form of protection.

It is, of course, better if the security staff can have forewarning of anyone approaching the perimeter fence, and this can be provided in a number of ways. Perhaps the best is the 'leaky cable' system, because it is completely invisible and undetectable. A pair of electric cables are buried and run around the perimeter some distance from the fence. Once buried they can be concealed by grass, bushes, even roadways and paths. They are called 'leaky' because the outer insulation is perforated so as to allow a magnetic field to be set up between the two lines when power is passed through them. Once the power is passing and a normal reaction level is established, the magnetic field acts as an invisible trip-wire. Anything which enters the field - human, animal, mechanical - will alter the magnetic flux and set up an imbalance between the two cables which will be revealed by a simple detector in the control room. The relative strength of this imbalance can be used to give an indication of the threat location and security staff can be mobilised so that by the time the threat arrives at the perimeter fence there is a reception committee waiting.

If this sort of system is backed by a few video cameras the security staff can have a very comprehensive idea of the nature of the threat before it even reaches the actual fence.

Clossur Stoperse Barrier

France

Stoperse (the name is derived from the French 'herse' - for harrow) is intended to prevent vehicles smashing their way through an ordinary gate. It ensures that vehicle bombs cannot be launched into an entrance, and will very definitely stop any wheeled vehicle attempting an illegal entry. It consists of two pits, dug into the road and reinforced with steel and concrete, covered with steel grids pivoted in their centres. In the normal position these form a secure flat platform across which a vehicle can safely drive. But on being set off, either by a sensor device or by manual control by a gate guard, the grids pivot down at their inner end, raising the end confronting the vehicle to about 45 degrees and revealing a row of sharp steel spikes. These are usually sufficient to shred the tyres of the vehicle, and the body strikes the steel grid and is stopped. A heavier or faster vehicle may rise and surmount the edge of the grid, but the tyres will still be in shreds and the front end will fall into the exposed pit or, if the momentum of the vehicle overcomes the locking mechanism and turns the grid back, then the rear wheels will drop into the pit. One way or another the vehicle is unlikely to get any further.

The Stoperse swings into the operating position.

Manufacturer: *Clossur SA, Pierre-Benite, France.*

A heavy truck with front tyres deflated and rear wheels trapped in the Stoperse barrier.

Scan-Tech Dynascreen Door USA

The **Dynascreen** is a walk-through metal detector of the sort used in most airports. There are three models: a lightweight, portable system which can be quickly set up in any convenient place; a standard fixed installation of more rugged construction; and a heavyweight installation with built-in shielding which makes it of particular value where the location has stray radio and magnetic fields which might otherwise result in false readings from the detection system. All models are of aluminium and have operating modes which are programmable for the detection of all metallic objects or merely for weapons, the sensitivity being adjustable within each mode. Once the settings and adjustments have been made the controls are key-locked and cannot be tampered with; any attempt at tampering or any disconnection of the power cable sounds an alarm.

Manufacturer: *Scan-Tech Security, Northvale, New Jersey, USA*

Right: *Scan-Tech Dynascreen archway metal detector.*

Koor 6000 Laser System   Israel

Koor 6000 laser system is a perimeter protection system which can either be permanently installed around a secure area or rapidly erected around a temporary site to give a continuous belt of invisible protection. The system consists of a series of posts which can be erected around the perimeter of the area. Each post carries a laser transmitter and a laser receiver, arranged so that when the posts are in place a laser beam (or beams) is directed from one post to the next so as to form an invisible fence around the area. The posts are wired to a central control point and may also be fitted with local audio alarms. Any object crossing the line of posts will interrupt the laser beams and cause a signal to be sent to the control unit, indicating that a break-in has occurred and also in which sector. At the same time the local audio alarms may be triggered to warn off the intruder, should that mode of operation be thought preferable. As with most of these computer-controlled systems, it can be set to run by itself, without demanding the constant attention of the operator; when a break-in takes place, an alarm sounds in the control room, bringing it to the operator's attention. The system can also be arranged to report by wire or radio to a distant control unit or to a police station or military post, according to the type of security in force.

One of the benefits of using a laser system is that it is impervious to weather or climatic conditions, resulting in a near-zero false alarm rate. This system is in use in several countries.

Manufacturer:
Koor Communications, Tel Aviv, Israel

The Koor 6000 system used to protect a parked aircraft.

Yael 15 Taut-Wire System

Israel

This is an alarm system which can be added to any existing type of perimeter fence, wall or gate, and consists of a number of taut wires woven inconspicuously into the fence or place on top of the wall or gate. These are connected, at intervals, to piezo-electric strain detectors which are wired to a central micro-processor unit. Any attempt to climb, cut or otherwise attack the fence or wall will result in the taut wires being disturbed. This will cause them to pull on the strain detectors, which will then signal to the controller that an attack is being made on that particular section of fence. Very sophisticated signal processing allows for the slight changes in strain due to heat or frost, wind, falling leaves, birds and similar natural phenomena, thus filtering out almost all false alarm signals.

Manufacturer: *Beta Engineering, Beer-Sheva, Israel*

Right:*The Yael taut-wire alarm system protecting a factory site.*

Portapungi Vehicle Barrier

The **Portapungi** is another device for preventing vehicles entering a secure area, guarding against every type of mobile threat from ram-raiders to vehicle bombs. A pit is excavated in the entrance road and a heavy steel framework is built into it, carrying a massive steel trunnion shaft. Steel prongs some four inches thick and about two feet long are attached to this shaft. The prongs normally lie flat, within a fixed steel framework, so that the two merge to form a solid floor across which a vehicle can safely pass. However, if a threat is perceived the gate guard can trigger the hydraulic mechanism which immediately lifts the prongs to an angle of about 45 degrees, facing the oncoming vehicle. The vehicle, if it does not stop, will be impaled on the prongs, which penetrate deeply into the vehicle body and usually remove the front axle completely. As the now wheel-less front end coasts across the top of the prongs, they rip into the underbody and always finally stop the vehicle by lodging against the rear axle.

Manufacturer: Western Industries, Bottineau, N Dak, USA.

A heavy truck with front axle removed and rear wheels blocked by the Portapungi.

Sentry 2000

Sentry 2000 is a portable protection system which can be set up anywhere within a few minutes to provide instant alarm if anyone approaches. It is ideal for protecting aircraft or vehicles which are temporarily parked, for conference halls and for VIP protection. The unit is entirely self-contained and takes the form of a pylon about one metre high which contains a passive infra-red detector, a micro-processor and a radio transmitter. There is also a rechargeable 12 volt battery with an operating life of 50 hours. The unit is simply placed on the ground, adjacent to whatever it is protecting, and then switched on. Thereafter any approach to the device will be detected by the dual-element pyro-electric sensor, which detects any change in the temperate caused by a human or a vehicle. Upon detecting such a change the micro-processor sends an alarm signal by radio to a control station where it is decoded to give an audio and visual signal to the control operator and, if necessary, can dial out to a reporting centre by means of a telephone line module.

Different models of the **Sentry 2000** have slightly different detection patterns in order to provide for various types of situation: the 5000, for example, has a detection zone which is longer and more narrow than that of the 2000. There is also a 'Scout' model which is shorter and fitted with a base spike so that it can be driven into the ground; it is also finished in camouflage colours so that it can be sited inconspicuously, whereas the normal **Sentry** is prominently coloured and marked to act as a visual deterrent.

Manufacturer:
RDS Electronics, Huntingdon, England

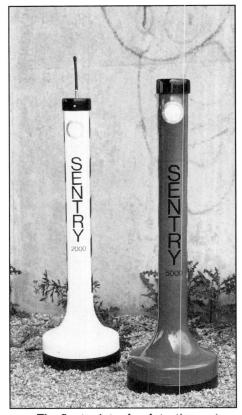

The Sentry intruder detection system.

The Sentry system in use, guarding a Russian fighter at Farnborough Air Show.

Cotag

Cotag is an abbreviation for 'coded tag', and the **Cotag** system uses radio-frequency coded tags which can be worn or carried or attached to anything which has to be positively identified. The tags contain active low-frequency transponders containing a microchip which stores information. This information largely consists of a unique code representing a serial number or an identity. The tag is normally quiescent; but when it comes within range of the electronic part of the **Cotag** system it is 'interrogated' and it automatically responds with its unique code. If this code is acceptable to the system, then the door opens, the vehicle barrier lifts, a counter checks off the individual's entry or any of several other actions, initiated by the interrogation and completed by computer-controlled relays, can be performed. One of the advantages of this system is that the individual does not actually have to do anything; he merely walks up to the gate wearing his tag, or carrying it on a key-ring. The interrogator checks as he gets within range and the door is unlocked for him to enter. Similarly, a tag can be fitted to authorised vehicles so that a ground loop can perform the interrogation and lift a barrier or open a gate.

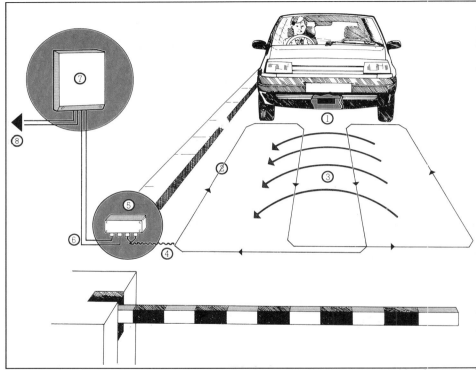

Diagram showing the Cotag principle. The Tag (1) on the car is interrogated by the ground coil (2) and its magnetic field (3), and, via the control system (4 - 8) opens the gate.

Manufacturer: Cotag International, Cambridge, England

Innofence

Israel

The **Innofence** is so-called because it is a fence which looks innocent. It has every appearance of an ordinary decorative fence, but it has a carefully-designed fibre-optic system built into it. The object is to provide a sound security system but not to make it obtrusive or even apparent, and the fence can be designed and manufactured in a varity of styles so that it complements the architecture and surroundings of the protected site. However, any attempt to climb over, break through, cut or otherwise disturb the fence will result in an alarm being given to a central control point.

Manufacturer:
Magal Security Systems, Yahud, Israel.

An example of the Innofence surrounding a factory.

61

Surveillance

Surveillance simply means 'watching', and all surveillance equipment is designed for doing just that, but in a covert manner. In general, it is taken to mean night vision equipment, radar, thermal imaging and similar technologies, most of which give the watcher a considerable advantage over the watched. It is for this reason that possession of such equipment is severely restricted in most of the European countries, lest the watched should acquire some of it and begin watching the watchers.

The history of modern surveillance equipment goes back to just before World War Two, when infra-red technology was examined in an attempt to use it as a method of detecting aircraft at night. This led to several improvements in detection devices but it was eventually superseded by the development of radar, though the German army sited infra-red equipment on the French coast which could detect ships at ranges up to 20 miles. Then both the German and American armies developed weapon sights which consisted of a spotlight delivering infra-red light, invisible to the naked eye, coupled to an infra-red sensitive sighting telescope, giving them the ability to fire at targets in pitch darkness at ranges up to about 200 yards.

This development lapsed after the war, but it was revived when seeker heads for missiles began to be developed, and most of the air-to-air and ground-to-air missiles eventually were to carry infra-red detection systems which could detect a hot engine and steer the missile into impact with it. This necessitated a rise to ever more sensitive detectors, and it had now become possible to rely upon the heat generated by the target instead of having to illuminate the target with infra-red light. This latter system known as 'active infra-red' remained in use with tanks for many years, with the tanks carrying a powerful IR searchlight and using an IR-sensitive sight. However, for applications where massive searchlight and power supply were inconvenient, active IR was no longer considered of much use.

The other system relying upon the target heat, became known, at first, as 'passive infra-red' and then 'thermal imaging' and it gradually was to improve to a point where a difference in temperature of half a degree Centigrade could be detected at several hundreds of yards range. Allied to this came developments in video technology so that the output of the **Thermal Imaging (TI)** Camera could be displayed on video screen in black and white with a remarkably fine degree of detail.

During this period a second contender had arisen and at first it looked as if it would so surpass infra-red as to render it obsolete; this was the technique known as **Image Intensification (II)**. A device, very similar to a television camera, scanning the target area could register the faint differences in the reflected light; these differences were then amplified by electronic means and were displayed on a phosphorised screen in order to provide a recognisable picture of the target. The amount of 'gain' or amplification given by this was in the region of 50 times the original contrast; by putting the displayed image through the same process a second time the gain became 50 x 50 = 2500, and by adding a yet third stage brought 50 x 50 x 50 = 125,000 times. This was the limit; attempts to add a fourth stage resulted in distortion and failure. However, a gain of 125,000 times provided a reasonably good picture, certainly good enough to be able to identify armoured vehicles at 500 yards range or shoot with accuracy against a man-sized target at 300 yards. And all this in starlight or dim moonlight. They would not work in pitch darkness, because there was no differential lighting to amplify, but for 95 percent of the time they were highly effective.

They had two defects; one, that they were bulky because of the three-stage requirement; and two, they often emitted a supersonic whistle which could not be heard by humans but which often upset animal life and, by their reaction, alerted the watched to the fact that something was not right. These were remedied by the 'second generation' sight which appeared in the early 1980s and used a new type of circuit, the 'micro-channel amplifier' which took up less space than a single stage of the first generation and yet produced almost as much gain as the three-stage device. The slight loss of gain was more than compensated for by the considerable loss in weight and size, resulting in highly efficient and light rifle sights and viewing devices.

This, roughly speaking, is where things stand at the moment, with **TI** in use where bulk is of little consequence, and second or third generation **II** for tasks where weight is of importance. The third generation **II** device is, simply, a second generation device with a much more sensitive display screen, resulting in a sharper and better contrasted picture. There are moves to develop **TI** sights for hand held weapons such as rifles, but there are considerable difficulties in getting the weight and bulk down to a size which does not interfere with the balance of the weapon.

Radar used as a surveillance device is another example of a specialised line of development. Radar as most people understand it is a long-range device for finding targets in the sky, but surveillance radar is primarily a short-rage device for finding targets on the ground amid a clutter of extraneous objects - buildings, trees, vehicles and anything else that might be in the way. The Doppler radar has become the principal instrument in this field since it ignores still, solid objects and concentrates on moving ones. The 'Doppler effect' relies upon the reflected radar signal returning at a higher, or lower, frequency than it left, due to the accelerating or slowing effect of the movement of the target, and the circuitry can be arranged to ignore returns at the

The night has eyes; tanks and their crews seen at night by thermal imaging camera.

returns at the transmitted frequency and indicate only those arriving back at a changed frequency. The signal is usually presented to the operator as an audio tone, and practice soon allows him to distinguish the tones from a walking or running man, a car, a tank or any other moving object. If we then make a further refinement and present a picture of the non-Doppler returns as a permanent picture on the screen, the moving targets can then be superimposed upon it and something resembling a coherent picture can emerge.

Video cameras have rapidly become a useful surveillance tool, principally because they can operate in a much lower light environment than conventional photographic cameras, and their output can be digitised and sent by wire or radio to a distant control room for instant evaluation. And a video camera allied to a thermal imaging device or with an image-intensifying lens becomes a highly sensitive information gathering machine in darkness or poor light. Computer enhancement of the images will give an additional stage in recognition in poor conditions, though this largely depends on the skill of the operator and is not something which can be applied in real time.

The computer can also provide a useful labour-saving property for video surveillance of a constant area. If the scene is photographed under the ideal conditions, with no people or vehicles in view, this image can be stored in memory. Thereafter the scene as viewed by the camera can be constantly compared with this ideal image. Instead of a human operator having to sit for hours on end looking at nothing very much until he gets bored and misses something, he can be doing some other task while the computer does the observing. As soon as there is any discrepancy between the stored image and the real-time image, an alarm can sound, drawing the operator's attention to the screen where the intruder, or intruders, will be highlighted for his instant recognition.

The drawback to all this electronic sophistication is, not surprisingly, the expense. It is hardly a mass market and very often a system has to be tailored to a specific site or task. As a result of this, the most common surveillance devices in the hands of most police forces are the simple video camera and the relatively inexpensive forms of hand night vision viewer.

Another expense, which is not always appreciated by the users, is that of maintenance. If you visit any exhibition of security equipment you will see video surveillance cameras providing images of the highest imaginable quality. And yet whenever evidence from a security video camera is shown on television, in order to apprehend a wanted criminal, the images are invariably grainy, fuzzy, of poor contrast, and generally resemble something from the earliest days of cinematography. Once installed, it seems, these cameras are thereafter left to clean themselves, adjust themselves and are generally neglected so long as they produce some sort of an image. As the old saying has it, the price of liberty is eternal vigilance, in more ways than one.

RASIT Radar   France

Rasit is a long-range (up to 40 km) ground surveillance radar for the detection of moving targets on or close to the ground, in all weathers. It is a pulse Doppler radar, operating in I/J band (8-20 GHz) and displays its information to the operator on a B-Scope, a cathode ray tube which indicates range by a scale on the left side of the tube and direction by a scale at the bottom of the tube. A target appears as a spot on the face of the tube which can then be related to the two scales to determine range and direction.

In fact, in **Rasit**, the tube is marked so as to give the target position in polar and UTM co-ordinates, so that the target can be rapidly related to a map. In addition, the Doppler sound which is generated by the target is transmitted to the operator either by loudspeaker or earphones, so that the operator can recognise the nature of the target, whether it be a walking man, a vehicle, a helicopter or a cow wandering across a field.

In order not to cause confusion the area under surveillance is split into sectors by a 'gating' system in the receiver. This means that only those responses from a particular selected 'slice' of the area - for example, from 5000 to 7500 metres, between 10° and 40°, will be displayed on the tube and in the earphones. This prevents confusion between two targets some considerable distance apart, and the 'slice' can be adjusted to positively pinpoint a specific target. An automatic alarm system can also be switched in, allowing the operator to eat or attend to other duties while the radar follows a preset search pattern; should it detect a moving target, then it locks on to it and sounds the alarm.

Very simple operating procedures mean that the operator does not have to be a highly-trained radar technician. It takes no more than ten seconds to scan a zone 20 km long and 120° wide, and less than 30 seconds to locate and identify a target. The unit comes in a variety of forms; the normal one is a four-

The Rasit surveillance radar.

66

unit pack which can be carried into action by three men and quickly fitted together, the antenna on a tripod, the power unit and control unit attached to it by cables. It can be mounted on a vehicle as a self-contained mobile surveillance device. Or it can be mounted on a balloon, using a two-axis gyroscope to keep the antenna pointed in the right direction irrespective of the movements of the tethered balloon. The balloon is flown at a height of up to 750 metres and the radar signals are sent down a cable to the control unit on the ground, allowing a high viewpoint to be obtained when the natural terrain would not otherwise permit it.

In actual service it has been shown that **Rasit** will detect a walking man at a range of 23 km, a car at 32 km, a 3-tonne truck at 40 km, a helicopter at 30 km and a low-flying aircraft at 40 km.

Manufacturer:
Thomson-CSF, Meudon, France

Rasit surveillance radar in field use.

Sopelem LISP Night Viewer

This French device is an excellent example of modular construction: by using a number of individual components which can be fitted together in different combinations it can provide the user with exactly what he requires without having to build a whole series of different devices. Basically it is a second-generation image intensifier, a tubular body containing an 18 mm diameter micro-amplifier. On the front of this is a lens giving unit power magnification, and alongside it is a battery box. On the rear end it is possible to fit a simple eyepiece, with dioptric adjustment to suit the user's eye, or a bi-ocular eyepiece which allows the user to see with both eyes, even though he is still looking through the single object lens at the front. If more magnification is needed an accessory lens module can be fitted on to the object lens, increasing the magnification to 3X but reducing the field of view from 40° to 12°. A face-mask can be fitted, so making it into a driving sight, or for use with an IR spotlight for aiming a weapon, and the focusing distance is such that it can even be used to read documents or maps etc., in near-darkness. In basic form, without the magnifying lens module, it weighs only 450 grammes and is 110 mm long.

Manufacturer:
Sopelem-Sofretec, Bezons, France

The Lisp viewer in its simple hand-held mode.

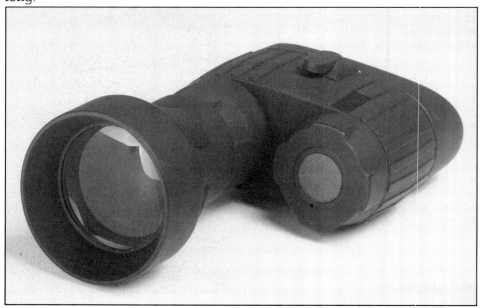

Radamec Series 2000 Surveillance System UK

The **Series 2000 system** is a highly flexible method of keeping a pre-defined area under permanent watch; it is thus ideal for coast-watching or frontier and border surveillance tasks. In brief, it consists of a master station and up to 50 sub-stations, which can be connected by radio, wire or fibre-optic links to the master station. The sub-stations can consist of whatever seems appropriate; radar, video cameras, thermal imaging cameras, laser rangefinders, gyro-compasses, low-light television are just some of the options. The prime requirement is, of course, that the output of the sensor devices is capable of being digitally transmitted to the master station; given that, anything can be employed. The sub-stations need to be sited to give overlapping fields of view, so that a moving target can be tracked from one station to another throughout the zone, and the master station can be located in a building or in a suitable vehicle in the field.

Manufacturer:
Radamec, Chertsey, England

An artist's impression of the Radamec 2000 system in operation.

Thermovision 880 TI Camera Sweden

This Swedish camera is an extremely sensitive device capable of detecting minute differences in temperature. The scanner unit converts infra-red radiation into a video signal which can then be sent by line or radio to a monitor unit for examination of the picture. The two models available, operating in either the 2 - 5.6 micron or the 8 - 12 micron wavelengths, allow the selected camera to match the particular task at hand. A number of different lenses are provided, so that fields of view from 2.5° to 40° can be chosen, allowing readings to be made over either wide areas or over smaller areas at longer ranges. The **Thermovision 880 TI camera** was actually designed for industrial use, where it is necessary to closely monitor temperature changes in a manufacturing process; but it also has applications in the surveillance field where extreme precision is required; as when attempting to defeat some forms of camouflage and concealment.

Manufacturer:
Agema Infra-Red, Danderyd, Sweden

The Agema Thermovision infra-red camera.

Hawkeye HT10 TI Camera UK

The **Hawkeye HT10 camera** is a thermal imaging camera which is more oriented towards surveillance and military use. Like most infra-red detectors it requires cooling, but instead of requiring cylinders of gas or separate cooling engines, it uses a unique closed-cycle cooling system driven by its own internal batteries, and it was the first such device to offer this refinement. It can detect virtually any kind of target, in complete darkness or reduced visibility, provided that there is a temperature difference between the target and its background, and it will produce a high-quality video picture even through smoke, haze or dust. There is a small monitor in the rear of the camera for the operator, but the output can also be displayed on a remote monitor in some secure position. There are many sorts of mountings, so that the unit can be fitted into vehicles or aircraft, or used on the ground as seen here. It can also be linked up to gyro-compasses, laser rangefinders and other observation aids, and has even been adapted as an anti-tank missile sight.

Manufacturer:
Hawkeye Systems, Hitchin, England

The Hawkeye thermal imaging camera (left) operating in conjunction with a laser rangefinder.

Signaal UA1242/02 night sight Video

Netherlands

One of the great drawbacks to any optical equipment is that as soon as you start looking through it, somebody else comes along and wants to have a look as well. I don't think the designers of this piece of equipment had that in mind, but they have solved the problem very nicely.

The **UA1242 viewer,** made by Signaal of the Netherlands, is a powerful image intensifier with an integral power supply, automatic brightness control, point highlight suppression and 5X magnification, and all weighing under 2 kg.

It was designed so that it could be easily and comfortably held and used for long periods. The automatic brightness control, like that of a TV set, ensures that as the viewer sweeps around his area the darker parts are given more amplification and the brighter parts less, so that he gets a constant level of brightness in his field of view.

Point highlight suppression is another ingenious piece of circuitry which overcomes one of the drawbacks of the earlier image intensifiers - if you had accidentally pointed it at a bright light, then the amplification would dazzle you and wipe out everything else on the screen for a few seconds. Suppression means that

the circuit detects a sudden bright light and shuts down the relevant part of the display so that the rest is not affected.

That is the basic instrument; the **UV1241/02** shown here adds a video camera and prisms to the night vision viewer so that the camera can see the picture as it is beingseen by the operator

Signaal UA1242 night vision viewer in standard form

and transmit it to another video monitor. This can be some distance away, say in a headquarters, or it can be close by for the convenience of those people who come along and want to have a look. In the former case it allows the commander an instant picture of what is happening on his front, and he can, by telephone or radio, direct the operator to point it at anything which takes his interest. In the latter case it allows the observer to get on with his own affairs uninterrupted by spectators.

The Signaal UA1242/02 night vision sight with video output.

Manufacturer: SIGNAAL-Usfa, Eindhoven, the Netherlands

73

Yuval Long Range TV Surveillance System   Israel

This is a long-range video detection and identification system which is capable of detecting a vehicle 35 km away and identifying its make and type at 25 km. There are two versions: **Yuval D** for use in daylight, and **Yuval D/N** for use by day or night.

The two systems both consist of a remote-controlled electro-optical head mounted on a motorised pan-and-tilt unit attached to a tripod or any other suitable platform, and a control unit which can be sited at any convenient point or mounted in a vehicle. The electro-optical head has two camera units, one for a wide field of view so that the operator can see a large area of his front and thus orient himself, and one for a narrow field of view which he uses for distant targets to examine them at a high magnification. Both units have automatic light control, giving optimum observation conditions, and the narrow field camera also has a range of optical filters which can improve the target-to-background contrast, can cut through haze and otherwise improve the image. The Yuval D/N also had additional image-intensifying circuitry which can be brought into play when the instrument is being used at night.

The control unit has two video monitors, one for each field of view, and the wide monitor carries a small image of the narrow field of view in a superimposed window.

The control unit also has all the controls used for steering the camera, selecting filters, changing the field of view and for fine focusing . There is also a video recorder, to allow the images to be kept for further analysis, and the images may also be transmitted to any number of points by radio or line.

Manufacturer:

Elbit Computers, Haifa, Israel

The Yuval long range video surveillance system

EL/M 2140 Radar   Israel

The **EL/M 2140** is a compact ground surveillance radar which can automatically detect vehicles out to a range of 33 km and personnel to 15 km. It can be set to watch any size of sector from a ten degree arc to a full circle and will scan it up to four times a minute. It is also possible to set a minimum speed for targets to be detected so that, for example, wandering animals can be excluded and only a quicker-moving vehicle picked up, so reducing the number of false alarms.

The EL/M 2140 equipment consists of a transmitter/receiver unit, an antenna assembly, and a display and control unit. It can be set up and put into operation inside ten minutes by two men, and the control unit can be up to 50 metres away from the transceiver/antenna. The control unit has a 10 inch colour video screen which gives a comprehensive map-like picture of the area under inspection; six different types of display are available, so that the operator can quickly switch to a clutter map, showing permanent returns, or to a UTM overlay so that coordinates can be taken off the screen, or to a target tracking mode or other functions. Seven area display scales can be used, including three magnified scales and a 0-30 km full screen scale. The operator has also, of course, full control of the antenna so that he can stop the scan and make a closer examination of any target that the radar has detected.

Various accessories are available to improve the utility: an electro-optical video unit can be fitted to the antenna so as to allow optical inspection of the chosen target if conditions permit; a modem allows digital transmission of the picture to a distant point; and a plotter will permit the screen display to be printed as a map for distribution.

Operating the EL/M-2140 surveillance radar.

Manufacturer:
Elta Electronics, Ashdod, Israel

IRIS: Infra-Red Imaging System

IRIS is a medium-range thermal imaging system which is completely self-contained and operates from a battery pack. It can be installed on a vehicle or man-carried. The TI camera image is displayed on a one-inch video screen at the rear of the instrument and is then viewed through a magnifying eyepiece. There is also a smaller version, MIRIS (Miniature IRIS) which is small enough to be hand-held and used for short-range observation.

Right: IRIS imaging system unit mounted above a weapon sight.

Manufacturer: Inframetrics Inc, North Billerica, Mass., USA

76

Litton M911 Night Vision System USA

The **M911** is a modular system primarily designed as a medium-range hand-held surveillance viewing device. The heart of the system is a second-generation image intensifier using a micro-channel amplifier which gives a gain in light intensity of 1200 times. This is contained on a module which also carries an infra-red light-emitting diode which provides covert light to illuminate up to about 6 metres distance, making it useful for map-reading, examining signs and similar short-distance observation. There is also a battery compartment, an off-on switch, and, at each end, interfaces for optical attachments.

On the front end a variety of object lenses can be attached to provide varying fields of view and degrees of magnification. For normal viewing these are specially-computed night vision lenses designed to extract the best possible image from the image intensifier. For less demanding roles there are C-mount adapters which allow commercial cine, still and video camera lenses to be fitted.

On the rear end of the module a standard optical eyepiece can be fitted, or a camera relay lens which will allow connection of virtually any commercial reflex 35 mm camera by means of the T-2 mount system. Another T-2 to C mount adapter will permit using video or cine cameras directly attached to the module.

Manufacturer: Litton Electron Devices, Tempe, Ariz., USA

Litton M911 body with camera relay lens and commercial video lens.

Litton M802-AA NVG

The M802 goggles were developed in cooperation with the United States army in order to provide passive night viewing in minimal light conditions. They are used for such tasks as driving vehicles, flying helicopters, air/sea search and rescue, and for close manual operations such as emergency vehicle repairs and maintenance, operating equipment in darkness and map-reading. The image intensifying tube is a second generation type giving a gain of 500 times, and the entire unit is self-contained and hands-free in operation. The total weight, including the batteries, is 850 g and the field of view of 40°.

Manufacturer: Litton Electron Devices, Tempe, Ariz., USA

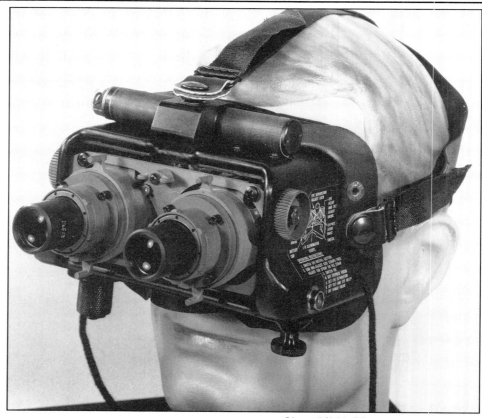

Litton M802-AA night vision goggles.

Leica BIM Pocketscope   Switzerland

This is a good representative of the pocket viewer class of night vision device, small enough to be carried in the pocket and used with one hand but with sufficient power to allow the user to look around his locality and detect anything within about 250 metres range and larger objects such as vehicles to even greater ranges. It was originally developed by Wild Heerbrugg, a Swiss company well known for surveying and other optical instruments; Wild merged with Leitz, of Leica camera fame, and are now known as Leica AGThe **BIM25 Pocketscope** is a simple combination of object lens, third generation micro-channel amplifier and eyepiece which gives no magnification, so that the viewer sees his surroundings in their natural size. The **BIM35** is similar but with an optical system giving 3X magnification; as a result it is somewhat larger.

Manufacturer:
Leica AG, Heerbrugg, Switzerland

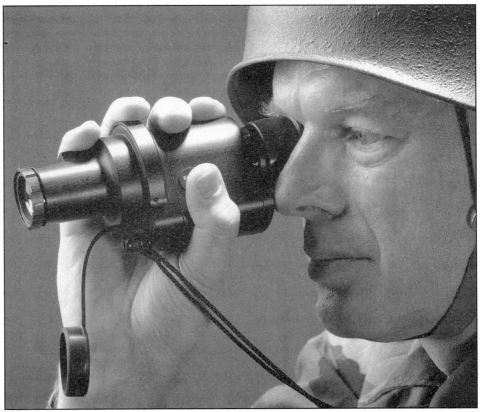

The small dimensions of the Leica BIM25 are obvious in this view.

Leica BIG35   Switzerland

Another Wild/Leitz product, the **BIG35** is an image-intensifying binocular capable of detecting a man-sized target in starlight to a range of about 700 metres. It uses a third-generation micro-channel amplifier and has a binocular eyepiece, giving two-eyed vision but through a single electro-optical unit. It weighs 1.5 kg, which is comparatively light for this type of instrument, and with a single 3 volt lithium battery can operate for up to 40 hours.

Caliope is a large and powerful thermal

The Leica BIG35 binocular in use by a tank commander.

Manufacturer:
LeicaAG, Heerbrugg, Switzerland

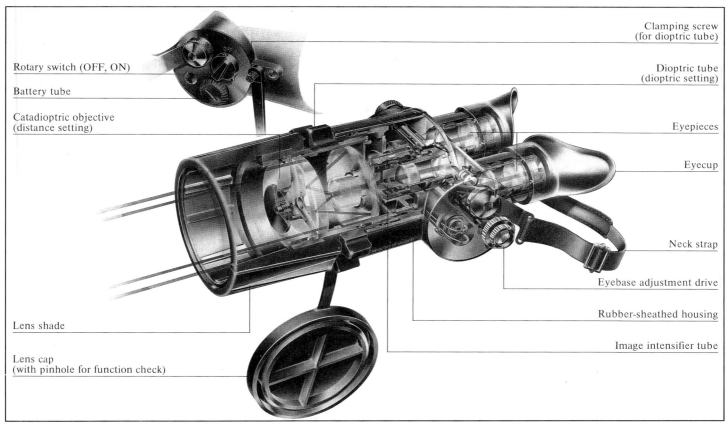

Clamping screw
(for dioptric tube)

Dioptric tube
(dioptric setting)

Eyepieces

Eyecup

Neck strap

Eyebase adjustment drive

Rubber-sheathed housing

Image intensifier tube

Rotary switch (OFF, ON)

Battery tube

Catadioptric objective
(distance setting)

Lens shade

Lens cap
(with pinhole for function check)

The internal arrangements of the Leica BIG35 binocular. (Leica AG)

81

Eurolook B2 Night Surveillance Sight Germany

The **Eurolook B2** is a compact and light weight night vision binocular for long range surveillance and observation. The main body contains a second-generation micro-amplifier tube with a gain of 1250 times. The objective lens is a 35 mm f/1.3 and behind the unit is a binocular eyepiece giving a total magnification of 3.8X and a field of view of 11 degrees. The entire unit weighs only 1.2 kg so that it can be carried and used for long periods of time without undue fatigue. It is capable of focusing as close as 10 feet away, and has the advantage of using easily replaceable commercial batteries as the power source.

Eurolook B2 night surveillance sight.

Manufacturer:
Euroatlas GmbH, Bremen, Germany

ARGUS Mobile Surveillance System UK

Argus is a mobile system designed for covert observation of some specific area, such as a frontier, a secure site, or a piece of ground upon which a clandestine aircraft may be expected to land. It can be quickly put into place from any convenient vehicle, can be equipped with any of a number of electro-optical sensors, and can function in all weathers for 24 hours a day. The sensor unit is tripod mounted and can easily be emplaced and concealed. The control unit, connected by a cable, can be up to 100 yards away and thus can be completely concealed from observation and the effects of weather.

The sensor unit can be selected to suit the task at hand, from a range including video cameras, thermal imagers, image intensifiers and laser rangefinders, any of which can be used alone or in conjunction with others.

Manufacturer:
Radamec, Chertsey, England

Argus mobile surveillance system deployed in the field.

Sopelem OB42 Binocular Viewer France

The **Sopelem OB42** night vision binoculars differ from most others of this class by being actual binoculars, i.e. having two completely separate optical paths, one for each eye, so that the natural stereoscopic effect is always present. The magnification is 4X and the gain is sufficient to allow the user to recognise a vehicle at 600 metres distance under an illumination level of one millilux, which is, in common terms, rather dim starlight.

A somewhat simpler version is the OB44 which uses a bi-ocular eyepiece operating through a single electro-optical system. This allows the user to use both eyes, which is less tiring than using one eye, but does not give a stereoscopic effect. However the ability to make a larger single image-intensifying tube does improve the performance, the OB44 being capable of identifying a tank at 1200 metres in starlight.

Manufacturer:
Sopelem-Sofretec, Bezons, France

Sopelem OB42 night vision binoculars.

Caliope TI Camera   France

Caliope is a large and powerful thermal imaging camera which is capable of detecting a vehicle at 6 km range and allowing positive identification at 2.5 km range. It operates by detecting the minute temperature differences between the target and its surroundings, and, of course, the greater the temperature contrast, the greater the chance of detection; vehicles are more easily spotted than individuals, because of the heat generated by their engines. Although they are primarily associated with observing in pitch darkness, these instruments are also very useful in daylight when visibility is poor due to mist or haze, allowing a hot-spot to be picked out, and they are also of great value in detecting targets concealed behind a thin screen of bushes or trees or behind camouflage nets. Such targets will evade detection by optical means, and very often by radar means as well, but they will inevitably produce a sudden hot spot on the scenery when viewed by this type of instrument.

Manufacturer:
Sopelem-Sofretec, Bezons, France

Caliope thermal imaging camera.

Area Sensor System for Intruder Classification and is described as an electronic observation system. It is designed to be installed in an area so as to detect any movement and to relay its findings to a controller who can be up to 5 miles away. It consists of two units, the sensor and the monitor. Up to eight sensors can be used with one monitor.

The sensor is attached to a transducer, which may be seismic, magnetic or infra-red so as to detect intruders from their movement, from the metal they carry or from the heat of their bodies or equipment. Any combination of these can be used within a system so as to cover all the possibilities. When the transducer is activated by the appropriate effect, the sensor sends a message to the hand-held monitor indicating the number of the sensor, the type of intrusion and the frequency of intrusion. Where large areas have to be covered, or where the monitor needs to be a considerable distance from the sensors, a relay unit can be installed which will extend the distance between sensors and monitor to 10 miles. A special High Power version can increase the working ranges to 10 and 20 miles.

Later additions to the **CLASSIC** system include a seismic cable which could be laid along a path or border and connected to a sensor, and a data output facility which permits the alarm message information to be passed to an external computer to permit graphic representation and other manipulation.

Manufacturer: Racal-Comsec, Salisbury, England

Burying one of the sensors for CLASSIC.

The **KN150** is a second-generation night observation binocular of the usual pattern, binocular only in the sense that both eyes view the output of the image intensifying tube; there is no stereoscopic vision effect as obtains in ordinary optical binoculars. Although there is no optical advantage over single-eye viewing, it is psychologically more comfortable and less liable to cause fatigue during prolonged observation. It is, though, a powerful device and can detect tanks at ranges up to 1500 yards in starlight.

Only two controls are fitted, an on/off switch and twist-grip focusing. An automatic timer will turn the power off after one minute so as to conserve power; however, the operator can temporarily override this if he is actually watching something. There is also an automatic brightness control system which cuts off the power if a sudden bright light, such as a flare or vehicle headlight, comes into the field of view. This prevents the operator being dazzled and thus losing his night vision capability. The circuit is restored after about one second's delay. The manufacturers do not quote an overall gain figure but it is probably in the 1250-1500X region. Optical magnification is 4X and the field of view is 8°. Standard commercial C-cell batteries are used, and the complete equipment weighs 2.6 kg.

Manufacturer:
Simrad Optronics, Oslo, Norway

The Simrad KN150 night observation device.

87

Detection Devices

Detection devices have become a major part of the anti-terrorist armoury in the past thirty years, and they have made vast strides in technology during that time. They can be traced back to the Polish mine detector of 1939. Buried anti-tank and anti-personnel mines had begun to make an appearance in the 1930s, and the Poles set about finding a reliable method of detecting them. Their solution was an 'inductive coil', a coil of wire through which an electric current was passed so as to generate a small magnetic field. Mounted on the end of a long handle, this coil was passed over the ground, so that the magnetic influence permeated the ground for some depth. Any metal found would distort the magnetic field, and a fairly simple electrical circuit translated this disturbance into a tone which sounded in the operator's headphones. Depending upon the position of the coil in relation to the metal object, the tone varied, so that the operator could tell very accurately where the object was situated and fairly accurately how big it was. All that remained was to uncover it, disarm it and remove it.

The counter-stroke to the Polish detector was to construct mines from wood, plastic, porcelain or papier-mâché so that there was no metal to detect. There was metal, in the form of springs and strikers, but not a sufficient mass of it to cause a major change in the magnetic field. So, the story of the metal detector since 1945 has been a gradual refining of the circuitry to the point where it will detect a one-inch nail buried two feet under concrete; until the development of micro-electronics, solid-state circuitry and all the other miracles which followed in the wake of the transistor.

The most recent developments which are still being explored and are not yet in production form, include the use of infra-red, magnetometer and radar technology. Infra-red detection relies upon the fact that a buried mine will have a different temperature to its surrounding earth, having absorbed and emitted warmth from the sun at a different rate. This can be detected with a sensitive infra-red camera or viewer or what is known as a 'multi-spectral detector' which can scan a variety of wavelengths. A magnetometer is really no more than a sophisticated variant of the original electronic mine detector, except that it is designed to detect any anomalies in the earth's magnetic field.

The original type of mine detector 'tuned out' the earth's magnetic effect and then looked for such things as a louder noise than the background - but the magnetometer looks at the entire picture and detects by seeking unnatural changes in the field.

Ground penetration radar is thought to be the most promising system of detecting mines, though it is not yet applicable to all circumstances since soil density and ground water have their effects upon the radar signal. In good ground it can detect both metallic and non-metallic mines; but it will also detect rocks and tree-roots, so there is some way to go before ground-penetration radar becomes a practical day-to-day operating system.

When the terrorist bombing of aircraft began, metal detectors were adopted but it was found that these were not satisfactory; passengers carried innocent metal objects in their baggage, and opening everything up to find innocuous metal items was time-wasting. The use of X-rays in examining suspect bombs had been in use for many years by bomb disposal engineers, and this technique was therefore adopted by the airlines, allowing them to quickly check the luggage of passengers for suspicious articles. An explosive device needed some method of setting it off, which usually involved timers or switches, batteries and wiring, and these could be fairly readily detected. But cunning terrorists disguised their bombs inside electrical devices - hair-dryers, tape recorders and such - so that the wiring appeared to be part of the innocent article. Moreover explosives were undetectable by simple X-rays. X-ray examination has been considerably refined in recent years. Colour displays give a rather more realistic picture, and careful selection of the energy source has made it possible to distinguish between various metals and also between chemical substances, some of which may be innocuous and some suspected of being explosives. So that seeing the inside of a tape recorder backed by a vivid colour announcing a nitro-compound gives rise for the suspicion that the article is really some electrical device carrying explosive.

Another line of attack is based upon the fact that explosives are mostly made with some form of solvent, and solvent evaporates over time. Sampling the air around a bomb will reveal the presence of a solvent, and thus suggest the presence of an explosive material; there are a few innocent substances that can give a similar reaction to an explosive solvent, but for the most part they are not substances which could be expected to be in normal baggage, so that an indication by an 'explosive sniffer' is fairly certain to reveal an explosive.

Dogs were originally used for this task, but recent years have seen a number of electronic machines capable of out-performing dogs and producing very reliable detection. It should be noted that there is no undetectable explosive; Semtex was hailed as such and was for some years indeed undetectable, but that was because the detection technique took time to develop and perfect. Semtex emits vapour like any other explosive, but in minute quantities and requires exceptionally sensitive methods.

So far the target had been the baggage, but there arose a new breed of terrorist, one who was either willing to sacrifice himself or who was willing to sacrifice an innocent victim by presenting them with a package to carry for onward delivery. It became necessary to examine passengers and their hand baggage more closely. Hand baggage merely went through the same detectors as did the checked baggage, while the passengers were directed through a gateway which carried metal detectors. These devices have improved considerably over the years; from being capable of detecting a gun they are now able to detect items as small as coins, tie-pins and cigarette lighters. In recent years an explosive sniffer has been added to many of these gateways, and these are sensitive enough to pick up any traces of explosive vapour lingering on the clothing or emanating from a bomb.

A new threat was added when small bombs began to be sent through the post. Postal authorities were not equipped to deal with this, and providing the necessary equipment took time; moreover the sheer volume of mail meant that selection had to be made between what looked suspicious and what did not. Therefore a new accessory came on to the market, the letter bomb detector, which was small enough to install in an office and simple enough to be operated members of staff. These are generally no more than simple X-ray devices which are intended to distinguish between innocuous letters and those which contain something to treat with caution. Once this determination has been made the suspect article is put aside for detailed examination by experts, the recipient having called the police to deal with it. These devices are not foolproof - they will sometimes, for example, react to books printed with metal-based inks - but the errors are always on the credit side in that they will often suspect an innocent package but scarcely ever pass anything remotely suspect.

AMD500 Portable Metal Detector

The **AMD500** is a rapid-deployment metal detecting archway which is lightweight and collapsible, so that it can be easily transported and set up in a few minutes. This makes it particularly useful when a search facility is suddenly required, as, for example, in an hotel where conferences may be held at irregular intervals, between which there is no secure requirement.

The sensitivity of the arch can be set to any of 12 levels, so as to tailor the unit to the specific requirement, and any detection is indicated by a red light and an audible alarm. In use, the arch is of ample size, giving an opening of 2m height and 33.5cm width. It can be collapsed into a package 1.02m long and 43cm wide, weighing less than 20kg, and it can be easily carried on the back seat of a car.

Two AMD500 metal detecting archways set up, together with their control units.

Manufacturer: Rapiscan Security Products, Crawley, England

90

Rapiscan

This is a conveyorised X-ray baggage inspection system which is in wide use in airports and other secure installations around the world. It is capable of detecting an item as small as a piece of 38-gauge wire, or of detecting through 17mm of steel plate. It is provided with computer-aided tracing and multi-energy facilities so that various methods of display can be applied on-screen in order to make images more distinct and more easily examined. Multi-energy systems permit the display of different materials in different colours, according to the atomic weight, and the system employed in this machine displays all explosives and similar materials in an orange colour, rapidly guiding the inspector's eye to any suspect area. The X-ray output is within all international safety margins and the system is safe for the passage of photographic film.

There are a number of models in the **Rapiscan** range, including a mobile unit housed in a trailer, a customized airport check-in desk system, and a vehicle inspection system.

The Rapiscan Model 2 baggage examiner, showing the control unit and monitor.

Manufacturer: Rapiscan Security Products, Crawley, England

TR Mail Explosives Detector No 2 UK

One of a range of mail detectors developed by Todd Research, this can be used in any office mail-room, requiring only the ordinary domestic power supply. It has the advantage of a larger search area than most office-type machines, a package 33 x 33cm being scanned in one pass. The screen shows the X-ray image of the item, and the machine is supplied complete with a recognition chart showing some of the more common types of letter bomb, to which the examiner can refer. If the package is dense, it is possible to step up the X-ray output to a high-intensity mode for a more detailed examination.

The Detector No 2 in use; the package is inserted by lifting the lockable flap in the front of the machine.

Manufacturer:
Todd Research, Chelmsford, England

AI Model 150 Explosives Detector UK

The **AI Model 150** is a hand-held explosives detector which runs from rechargeable batteries or from an AC mains supply. It has dual sensitivity settings and is ready to use within a few seconds of switching on. In use, it is swept across the person or package and will detect minute amounts of explosive vapour, giving an indication by a red light visible to the operator and by an audible alarm. The design ensures that such things as perfume and cleaning fluid do not raise false alarms. A general-purpose nozzle can be fitted to permit sampling the inside of bags and packages and a personal probe for searching beneath clothing.

The instrument is simple to use and requires very little training of the operator. A series of LED indicators give a constant check on the status of the instrument, and it can run for up to eight hours on a single battery charge.

Manufacturer:
Rapiscan Security Products, Crawley, England

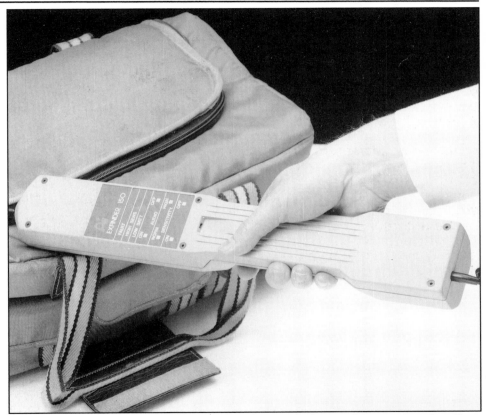

The Model 150 explosives detector being used to examine a handbag.

SDSE Scanna Letter Bomb Detector UK

The **Scanna** is a desk-top unit which can inspect letters, packages and parcels up to 400mm wide and 57mm thick as fast as they can be loaded into it. It will detect letter bomb devices but is programmed to ignore such common items as paper-clips, staples and so forth which can usually be found in commercial correspondence. The unit is powered by the ordinary domestic electricity supply and requires no specialist training. There are no manual tuning controls, and a simple ten-second set-up routine confirms the instrument is working correctly. There is no health risk to the operator, nor any risk to photographic or magnetic media in the packages.

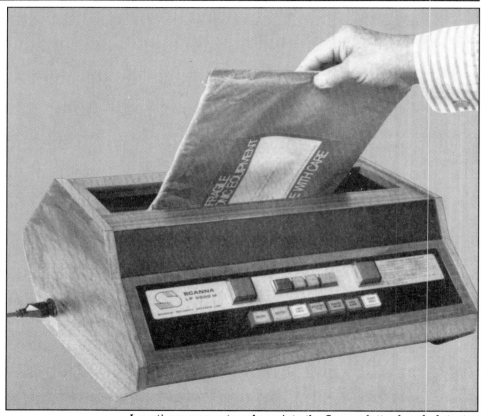

Inserting a suspect package into the Scanna letter bomb detector.

Manufacturer:
S & D Security, London, England

94

Mailcheck 200 Mail Screening System

The **Mailcheck 200** is a miniaturised conveyor screening X-ray system for the rapid examination of small hand baggage, letters and parcels. It contains a small X-ray generator, an internal radiation shield, an electrically driven conveyor belt and a viewing screen. The items to be examined are placed on the belt, moved into the machine, and then a safety door over the belt is closed; until this door is closed there can be no X-ray emission. The control lever which closes the door then switches on the X-ray generator, the rays pass through the object, and the image is displayed on the screen. This is then reflected to a viewing hood in front of the operator so that there can be no direct path between the X-ray generator and the operator. The level of emission is less than that of a domestic television set.

The whole unit is 57cm high, 55cm wide and 64cm deep and weighs 80kg. Packages up to 275 x 80mm can be examined, though larger packages can be screened by opening a rear panel.

Manufacturer: Rapiscan Security Products, Crawley, England

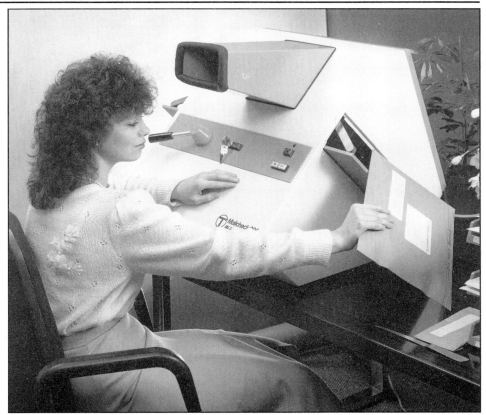

Loading the Mailcheck 200; the lever on the front panel closes the door and then switches on the X-ray source.

ITI ML-1 Detector

USA

This is a conventional metal detector but built to a very stringent specification to suit it to the harsh use expected in military and security applications. The detector is watertight and mounted on the end of a telescoping shaft, the electronic circuitry being inside another sealed box close to the handle end of the shaft. The unit is supplied complete with a carrying case and a pair of earphones for the operator.

The **ML-1** emits an electro-magnetic field from the detector coil; this permeates the ground and is distorted by the presence of any metallic object. This disturbance is detected and converted into an audio signal in the earphones. The instrument is sensitive to all types of metal, including iron, steel, gold, copper, brass and silver. The coil diameter is 305mm and the entire unit, complete with its four 1.5 volt C cell batteries, weighs 2.8kg.

Manufacturer: Ion Track Instruments, Burlington MA, USA

The ITI ML-7 metal detector, showing the electronics unit mounted close to the handle.

HED Explosives Detector

This is a hand-held battery operated device which can be used to examine vehicles, freight containers, aircraft and similar objects for the presence of explosives. It is capable of detecting explosive material inside closed metalwork such as car doors or fuel tanks and will also search interior walls, floors and ceilings without the need for dismantling or damage. It can also be used to search for drugs and other materials.

The unit consists of a hand-held probe connected to an electronics unit carried or worn by the operator. The probe carries a small radioactive source and a neutron chamber. The radioactive source emits neutrons which will pass through any substance but which will be scattered by any hydrogen-bearing material; these low-energy neutrons are detected, and their presence is an indication of a suspect material. The detection is electronically registered and converted to an audio signal in the operator's earphone. Detection is not affected by the substance intervening between the probe and the suspect material; it can be solid steel or an air-space without showing any observable difference in sensitivity.

Manufacturer:
S & D Security, London, England

Examining a car door with the HED explosives detector.

97

Bucky X-Ray

The **Bucky X-ray** system comprises a generator and a protective shield which incorporates a fluorescent screen.

The generator is a complete self-contained unit with the X-ray tube, high voltage generator and controls in a single box. The electrical units are enclosed in a lead cage and are oil-immersed so that radiation leakage is kept to a minimum and the unit is adequately cooled. The X-ray generator is a continuous unit, though it has the ability to emit pulsed energy for certain applications. There are 12 pulse durations available, and four high-voltage settings delivering greater or lesser penetration, so that almost any kind of target can be successfully penetrated. There is also an adjustable electronic timer which can be set to allow repetitive exposures for a number of similar items, avoiding the need to reset the exposure time for every item.

The generator is used in conjunction with the protective shield. This provides protection to the operator, can be used in direct sunlight, and can be carried and set up by one man. Two sizes are available, the Model A which allows large objects like suitcases to be examined, and the Model B for smaller items such as briefcases and postal packages.

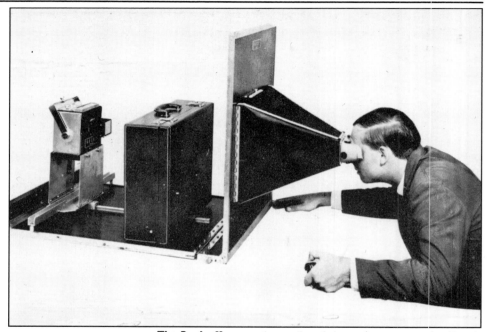

The Bucky X-ray system set up to examine a suspect suitcase.

Manufacturer:
Bucky X-Ray International, NY, USA

Vallon 1612 Metal Detector   Germany

The **Vallon** 1612 metal detector is of the usual electro-magnetic field type, and the advanced integrated circuit system ensures reliable detection of all ferrous and non-ferrous metals on or under the ground. The search coil, 305mm in diameter, is mounted at the end of a telescopic carrying bar which can be easily adjusted to suit the operator. A handle and retaining elbow clamp allow the unit to be used in one hand very easily without the bar being attached to the operator. The electronics are carried in a belt pouch, and the rigid earphone can be worn on the head or simply clamped to the man's jacket, the two-stage volume control allowing the output to be heard quite easily.

A more recent version, the **1612H**, uses an oval search coil, the makers claiming that such a shape ensures a very precise localisation of small objects without having to slow the detection speed. The head is also sealed against the ingress of water so that it can be used to search stream beds or ponds.

Right: *Searching a track, using the Vallon 1612H metal detector.*

Manufacturer: Vallon GmbH, Eningen, Germany

Heimann Hi-Scan 9080TS

USA

The **Hi-Scan 9080TS** is an X-ray baggage examination system which can cope with packages up to 914mm x 812mm. It uses an advanced technology which allows the examiner to 'see' objects through 13mm of steel plate, so that its application to everyday baggage poses no problems. The X-ray image is processed into a picture with 20 grey tones, so giving a much finer definition, and the availability of 2:1 magnification also allows a more detailed examination of suspect areas. Since it operates on a much lower X-ray power than comparable units, the X-ray generator has an estimated life of over 20,000 hours of operation; this lower operating current also means much lower radiation than other systems.

An optional voltage stabiliser is available for localities where the available electrical supply is prone to fluctuation, and 'pseudo-colour' imaging, in which various elements in the picture are displayed in different colours, can also be provided.

Manufacturer:
Heimann Systems, Iselin, NJ, USA

The Heimann baggage examiner in use; the second monitor provides a 2 x magnification without needing to switch pictures on a single monitor.

100

Controlix 2D Luggage Examiner France

The **Controlix 2D** is another X-ray baggage examiner, but one which shows a different approach to the problem. An X-ray generator directs a narrow vertical beam of energy to the baggage conveyor. Two rows of photo-sensitive cells are installed in the walls opposite the generator and as the baggage passes, so a line at a time is examined and transmitted through the moving object, stored, and then assembled to present a complete picture on the monitor. This linear scanning by a narrow beam reduces the amount of radiation required for efficient scanning.

The controls can be set to a 'critical absorption threshold' which causes suspect areas to blink as they are presented on the screen, so directing the examiner's attention to them. In order to make a more thorough investigation the examiner can select 14 different contrast ranges and up to 256 grey steps in the picture.

The unit is provided with wheels, so that it can be easily moved into any desired position, and jacks which allow it to be adjusted for height so as to conform with existing conveyor systems or other furnishing.

Manufacturer:
Schlumberger Industries, Rungis, France

A bank of Controlix 2D baggage examiners, together with archway metal detectors, in use at an airport.

Explosive Ordnance Disposal

Thirty years ago explosive ordnance disposal (EOD) was a scarcely-known military activity which was almost entirely concerned with disposing of unexploded munitions, relics of the two world wars, found on building sites or in the attics of recently-deceased old soldiers. International terrorism has swept all that away (although it still represents the bread and butter of the EOD operator) and today the emphasis is on terrorist bombs. These make things infinitely more difficult; with wartime ordnance there is usually, somewhere, a drawing of the device and a description, so that at least the operator knows what he is dealing with and can work out the easiest and safest way to go about it. With terrorist devices the mechanism is completely unknown and the operator simply has to approach it in the assumption that whatever he does might be the very thing that the bomb-maker selected as his method of initiating the explosion, be it movement, light, noise or some other effect.

This has led to the perfection of a variety of remote-control devices to allow the operator to work on the bomb in some degree of safety. The Morfax Wheelbarrow was the first of these, a little tracked vehicle which could be driven up to the bomb and carried a video camera so that the operator could examine it from a distance. Then came shotguns that could blast away the bomb's wiring before it had time to fire the detonator, mechanical hands and grips which could perform operations on the bomb, and a lot of other things which the EOD operators prefer not to talk about. For a great deal of the EOD world is kept secret, since it is obviously unwise to display all the cards in one's hand at the commencement of the game. That being the case, you must excuse us for dealing with this equipment in the most general of terms.

Right: A U.S. Army EOD suit; note the collar and groin protection.

An **EOD suit** is an armoured suit intended to preserve the EOD operator from the worst effects of a bomb which might blow up while he is working on it. He may very well suffer injuries, but they will be considerably less than those he would have suffered without the suit, and it will almost certainly save his life, provided the bomb is not of an outrageous size.

Different manufacturers have different ideas, but, in general, an EOD suit consists of a helmet, jacket, trousers and boots. The helmet needs to be fully adjustable and also to have a highly efficient suspension and shock-absorbing system to withstand close-range blast. It will also need a strong visor to protect the face, communications equipment access such as built-in earphones, and possibly a forced-air blower system to keep the operator cool and keep his visor clear of condensation.

The jacket will be of flexible aramid fibre armour, encased in a waterproof and ultra-violet proof cover and then in a cloth garment. It should open at the side, so as to present an unbroken front surface, and it should carry pouches into which ceramic or steel protective plates can be inserted. There should be a thick and relatively stiff collar to protect the neck and under the chin, and an ample apron to protect the groin, for psychological reasons if nothing else. Pouches for tools, radios, air supplies and so forth need to be incorporated into

the design but carefully thought out so that their presence does not hinder the operator.

The trousers are also of multi-layer aramid fibre cloth, and the boots really form an extension to this, using aramid fibre for the legs and boot uppers and

compound aramid/resin for the boot soles. Gauntlets can be provided, but most operators prefer to work with their bare hands, and gauntlets are really only of use when lifting a suspect object into a bomb trailer or moving it into a better position to work on it, both of which are uncommon.

A British EOD operator examining a package. The pouch on the back is for radio equipment.

DSM1 Clock Detector Serbia

One method of discovering a bomb is to find out whether there is a timing device working in the area; if there is, and all legitimate timing devices are discounted, then a bomb is a likely explanation. This Serbian detector uses microwaves to detect the operation of any quartz or mechanical timing device, and it also includes a highly sensitive electronic stethoscope for making critical examination of suspect devices. Careful use of the microwave unit can indicate the area in which the timing device lies, and closer examination with the stethoscope will pinpoint its position.

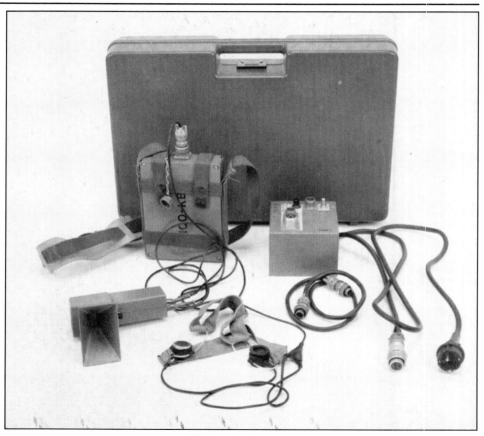

Manufacturer: Institute of Security, Belgrade, Serbia

The DSM1 clock detector and associated stethoscopes.

Model 1152 Disruptor — Serbia

It may sound odd, but one of the quickest and easiest methods of neutralising a bomb is to blow it to pieces; not simply by placing a charge against it, but by very carefully and selectively firing a projectile into it so as to destroy the switching or timing or firing device before it has time to function. Needless to say it has to be done very precisely, by somebody who knows exactly what he is doing, otherwise the whole thing becomes very embarrassing for all concerned.

The device used to do this trick is called a 'disruptor', since that is just what it does - it disrupts the mechanism of the bomb without affecting the explosive. And because the trick has risks, it can hardly be done by walking up to it with the disruptor in hand and firing it. So the disruptor fits on to an adjustable stand, so that it can be very accurately aimed at a particular spot. It consists simply of a barrel and a chamber; unscrewing the end of the chamber allows a cartridge and projectile to be loaded, after which the cap is screwed back on and an electric firing device fitted and wired up. The operator then retires to a safe distance and fires the device. Alternatively it can be carried into place by a robot, aimed by video camera and fired by remote control. The 'projectile' can be one of several alternatives; half a litre of water can do surprising damage when launched at high velocity, and there is no danger of it ricocheting off to do damage elsewhere.

Manufacturer:
Institute of Security, Belgrade, Serbia

This disruptor can use two barrels simultaneously in order to deal with multiple firing devices.

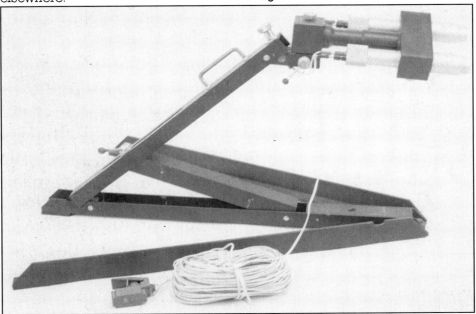

Bomb trailers are specially reinforced trailers into which bombs or suspect articles can be placed and then removed to somewhere remote to be either dismantled or destroyed. They are designed so that the container for the bomb will confine the blast from moving sideways and vent it upwards where, it is hoped, it will do little damage.

The **PE3K bomb trailer** is from Serbia and is a fairly simple device, little more than a heavy steel container on a heavy steel bed, supported by four wheels. There is a small hand-operated hoist for lowering the bomb into the container and a canister of fire extinguishing equipment for dealing with any incendiary device which ignites while in transit. The container can withstand the detonation of 3kg of TNT.

The **SA600** is from the USA and is to a rather more luxurious specification. The blast container is double, with an internal replaceable chamber, and the winch and hoist can be remote controlled by wire or radio. The hoist also has an automatic mechanism which ensures that the load is placed in the exact centre of the container when it is lowered. The trailer has heavy duty leaf springs and the special tyres are heavily reinforced with nylon so as to withstand the downward thrust should the load detonate. The trailer is capable of withstanding the detonation of 33 8-inch sticks of dynamite without damage.

Below: *The SA600 bomb trailer with its hoist folded down across the wheels.*
Manufacturer: Sas R&D, Miami FL, USA

Opposite: *The PE3K bomb trailer, with a device being hoisted up to load.*
Manufacturer: Institute of Security, Belgrade, Serbia

Cyclops EOD Robot

This is a small remote-controlled robot which can get into places which larger models cannot reach; for example it can go down the central gangway of an omnibus or aircraft, through shop and house doors, and, with its front track extension, can negotiate stairways. It can turn in its own length and with its operating platform folded down can pass underneath a desk. The operating platform can be raised to a height of 1.2 metres and can carry almost anything from a video camera to a disruptor, and the top of the platform has a tilting head so that whatever is on it can be accurately directed. Driven by an electric motor, the robot has sufficient power to tow heavy packages away from vulnerable areas.

Control is performed either by means of a cable which the robot pulls behind it, or by radio link. When carrying a video camera the signals can be transmitted back to the controller either by the same cable or by a second radio link.

Right: *The Cyclops EOD robot with operating head raised and carrying a camera.*

Manufacturer:
IMVEC, Alton, England, UK

Pedsco RM1 Robot Canada

Most robots are tracked, but there is no reason why a wheeled robot should not be just as efficient in most applications, and it will certainly be less expensive. This Canadian design carries the usual type of manipulator arm which can be fitted to carry a disruptor, a shotgun (the 'poor man's disruptor'), hook, grab, X-ray source or stethoscpes for handling almost any EOD task. A video camera and floodlight are fitted as standard. The operator has a portable monitor and cable unit, and controls the robot from a safe distance. As the robot moves, so it drags out cable from the monitor console. Power is supplied by a vehicle battery on board the robot.

The Pedsco robot examines a suspicious article; the operator would normally, of course, be somewhat farther away.

Manufacturer: Pedsco Canada Ltd, Scarborough, Ontario, Canada

109

TSR80 Hornet EOD Robot Israel

Another batterydriven lightweight, this can be carried easily in the back of most cars, and it will serve to introduce a new phrase: 'degrees of freedom', which tells us how much flexibility the manipulating arm has. This has five degrees of freedom: 1, the first arm, pivoting on the robot body, can rise and fall; 2, the second arm hinges on the first; 3, the third arm hinges on the second; 4, the third arm can extend; 5, the operating head on the third arm can twist. This allows the operator a great deal of choice in manipulating whatever is held on the operating head into all sorts of positions. Two video cameras are mounted, one on the operating head so as to be able to precisely position whatever is being carried, and the other at the rear of the third arm, on a pan and tilt head, so that the operator can look all around for a general view of the scene. Control is by radio link, and it can be controlled out to a range of 1.5km. All the usual attachments can be fitted.

The TSR80 robot with its monitor and control unit.

Manufacturer:
21st Century Sivan Ltd, Tel Aviv, Israel

The TSR80 peers underneath a car, demonstrating its flexibility.

AI Security Ro-Veh EOD Robot   UK

The **Ro-Veh** was developed after careful study of existing robots, with the aim of capitalising on all the good points and reducing the weak points. It can be in tracked or wheeled form; the tracked unit is recommended for all-terrain work, but where surfaces are smooth the wheeled vehicle can operate more quickly. The vehicle is electrically driven, power being supplied down an umbilical cable from either a portable generator or a converted domestic supply. The same cable carries all the control signals, but uses a multiplexing system for control and thus requires no more than four wires in the cable, resulting in a light and very flexible cable which does not hamper the vehicle's movements. Speed control is by a joystick and is very precise, allowing the vehicle to be positioned within a few millimetres.

The vehicle carries an articulated double boom with large angles of travel, and the design is modular, allowing extra lengths to be attached to limits imposed by stability. All the usual types of apparatus can be fitted to the boom, and there is also a charge dropper which permits an explosive charge to be laid and then the vehicle withdrawn, laying a firing cable behind it. A video camera is fitted on the boom, with a zoom lens, and a second camera can be fitted on the body as a driving aid for when the boom camera is pointed elsewhere.

Manufacturer: AI Cambridge Ltd, Cambridge, England

The Ro-Veh in wheeled form, carrying a shotgun and two disruptors.

112

Morfax Wheelbarrow EOD Robot UK

Morfax were the originators of the **EOD robot**, which was adopted by the British Army in 1974 under the code-name **'Wheelbarrow'**. Their original design has been improved over many years of operational experience, and the model shown here is known as the 'Super M'. This is a well-tried and reliable vehicle capable of mounting a wide variety of devices, including shotguns, disruptors, manipulators and car-towing systems.

It also has the ability to carry an X-ray system which, by video link, can deliver real-time images to the control unit monitor. Various camera assemblies can be fitted, to deal with particular tasks, and the track system is designed with 'variable geometry' so that it can be readily altered to allow it to negotiate particularly difficult terrain or climb stairs.

The Morfax Super M Wheelbarrow mounting a Browning automatic shotgun.

Manufacturer:
Morfax Ltd, London, England

Alvis Wheelbarrow EOD Robot UK

Alvis also manufacture the **Wheelbarrow** for the British Army, their version being known as the **Mark 8 Robot.** It uses a light alloy body and stainless-steel rubber-shod tracks, driven by two 12 volt batteries. Drive is via a two-speed gearbox, and steering by differential track action. The hull can be moved forwards or backwards relative to the tracks, so as to alter the centre of gravity and thus adjust the balance of the vehicle when negotiating difficult terrain. The body carries a moveable H-frame which incorporates various actuators and terminates in an extendible manipulator arm. Two cameras, each with its own spotlight, can be fitted. The vehicle is controlled from a hand control panel, linked by radio, wire or fibre-optic cable; radio is the preferred system, allowing a range of up to 1km in open country, less in urban areas. Alternatively, a 150 metre cable link can be used.

Operational accessories used on Wheelbarrow include all the usual disruptors, shotguns, hooks, grabs and towing devices.

Manufacturer: Alvis Logistics Ltd, Coventry, England

114

Opposite above: This is the 'Improved Wheelbarrow Mk 8' with some differences in track suspension.

Opposite below: An extra-reach boom can be fitted to Wheelbarrow Mk 8 to allow it to reach into positions frequently inaccessible to other types of robot.

Wheelbarrow Mark 8 with its accessories and H-Frame.

Blaster EOD Robot

Blaster was developed to meet a requirement from the Norwegian Army for a vehicle capable of performing EOD tasks, firefighting, rescue and remote observation, and its design was influenced by several years of experience in developing underwater search equipment. The basic machine is very robust, and the unusually wide tracks give it excellent stability in all types of ground and particularly good flotation over soft ground and bogs. The manipulator arm has seven degrees of freedom, giving it great versatility, and it can lift 100kg and tow cars. A built-in battery pack gives up to 5 hours of continuous operation before requiring a change, or, alternatively, it can be supplied with power by means of an external cable. Control from the remote console can be done by radio or by cable link. there is the usual wide selection of operational equipment which can be fitted to the manipulator arm to perform any desired function.

Manufacturer: Remote Systems AS, Saebvåg, Norway

Blaster fitted with a lifting grab.

Blaster, with its control console.

Auto-Robo RM-35   France

The **Auto-Robo** is a small, powerful, and relatively simple vehicle which can be adapted to carry a disruptor, a shotgun or a gripping claw in the manipulator arm. There is also a laser sighting system which allows very precise aiming of the disruptor or shotgun or placing of a charge. An 8mm CCD video camera is fitted above the arm to give the operator full command of the machine's actions, and lights are also provided. Optional extras include colour video cameras, an X-ray system, a pneumatic anti-recoil system for mounting disruptors, and a number of special adapters to allow different weapons to be carried.

Battery driven, the **RM-35** is controlled by either radio or cable, and is compact enough to be carried in a small car. It uses a large number of standard commercial automobile components so as to allow easy maintenance and repair.

The RM-35 with shotgun and operating claw mounted.

Manufacturer:
Auto-Robo, Domene, France

118

Kentree Hobo Robot   Ireland

Another wheeled robot, the **Kentree Hobo** is currently in use with over 34 agencies in 22 countries, including the United Nations. The six wheels are independently driven and torsion-bar suspended, giving it the ability to overcome the worst terrain without wheel-slip. Operated by radio, it can be controlled to over 1000 metres distance, or it can be cable controlled. A standard 150m cable is supplied, but additional cables out to 500m distance can be added. There are three video cameras fitted as standard, and the manipulator arm has six degrees of freedom, one of which is 440° rotation of the entire manipulator on a turret base fitted to the top deck of the vehicle.

The power supply is by on-board batteries, and a battery charger is provided. The control console is fitted with a video monitor, vehicle functions and options controls, DC and AC voltage inputs and video output for driving additional monitors. Separate control consoles for radio and cable operation are provided.

Manufacturer: Kentree Ltd, Kilbrittan, Ireland

The Hobo fitted with the standard manipulator claw. This very capable robot can also be equipped with a multitude of extras which include gun mountings and car towing attachments. (As previously marketed by Royal Ordnance plc)

Standard EOD Robot

The **Standard EOD robot** is currently in use by the US Army and is a lightweight model with an electric motor driving each track, thus providing both motive power and steering ability. The manipulator arm has five degrees of freedom and is provided with attachments for disruptors, shotguns, laser designator, acoustic sensors, X-ray unit, charge-positioning unit and other devices. A colour video camera is permanently fitted, and control can be performed either by radio or by fibre-optic link. Using radio the robot can be operated at a distance of about 300 metres; with fibre-optic cable this is reduced to 100 metres.

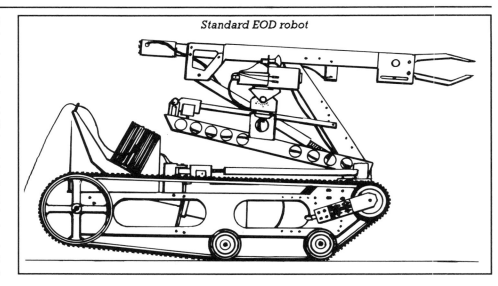

Standard EOD robot

Manufacturer:
Standard Manufacturing Co, Dallas TX, USA

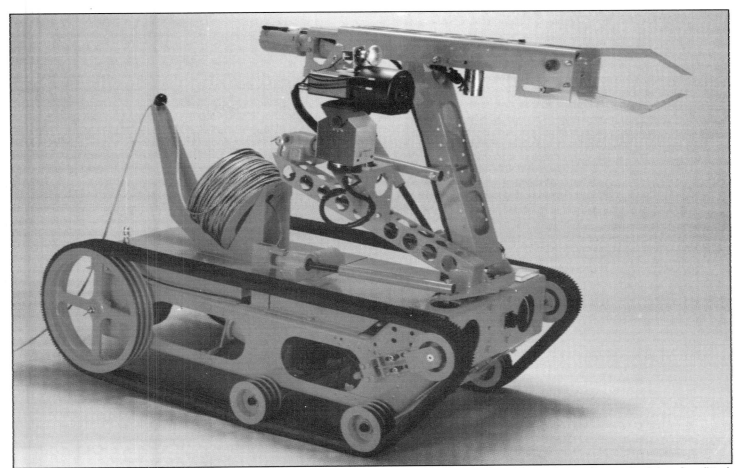

The Standard robot, with fibre-optic cable control and a manipulator claw fitted.

TR Mini Transportex X-Ray Unit

The **Mini Transportex** is a lightweight transportable X-ray unit consisting of an X-ray transmitter, a receiver, a video camera and a video monitor. The entire apparatus can be carried in a car and powered by the car's 12 volt battery. Its prime purpose is the examination of strange or suspect packages without moving them. The X-ray transmitter is placed on one side of the package, the receiver on the other. The receiver consists of a sensitive screen upon which the X-ray image is projected after the rays have passed through the package, and this image is then captured by the video camera and transmitted down a cable to the monitor, which can be set up at a safe distance. Once the contents of the package can be seen and studied, the necessary action can be taken to call up an EOD unit if required.

The system can obviously be used for examination of anything; it could, in an emergency, be set up to examine baggage or mail or any other material in situations where it would be inconvenient to take the material to a permanently set up examination system.

Manufacturer:
Rapiscan Security Products, Crawley, England

The Mini Transportex in use; the video unit is behind the suspect dustbin, the EOD man is positioning the X-ray source, and the screen picture can be seen below.

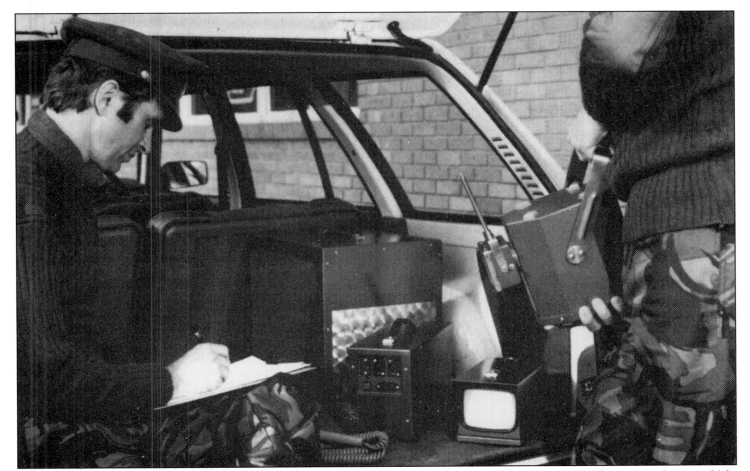

Unloading the Mini Transportex from a vehicle.

Allen Hook & Line Set

After all the foregoing displays of technological versatility, it is as well to remember that not every EOD operator has a robot at his beck and call, and that many of the more routine tasks can be performed with simple equipment. The **Allen Hook and Line Set** is an example of this basic equipment. It is, in fact, essential equipment for any EOD operator, allowing him to handle or lift or move potentially dangerous items, move objects out of the way so as to obtain a clear view of his target, or in extreme cases lower himself or be lowered down to investigate something in an otherwise inaccessible position, or for a thousand and one other mundane but vital tasks. As the picture shows, the kit contains an astonishing selection of hooks, clamps, lines, strops, vacuum suckers, clips and cables which experience has shown can be of the utmost importance at the scene of a bomb disposal task. It may not be glamorous or high-tech, but it is among the hardest-worked pieces of the EOD man's toolkit.

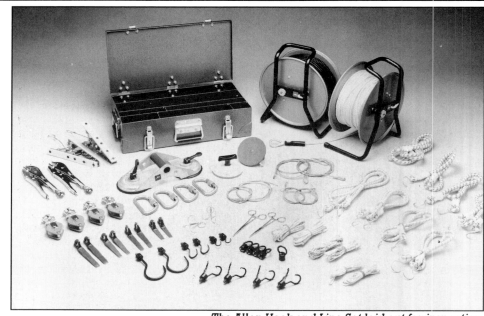

The Allen Hook and Line Set laid out for inspection.

Manufacturer:
Allen & Co, Evesham, England

124

Specialised Vehicles

For their everyday work of catching criminals and keeping the peace, police forces need no more than standard commercial vehicles, slightly modified to carry radios and other specialised equipment. But to deal with terrorist incidents, riots and 'civil disturbances' they need something more resistant to attack and therefore find themselves in a dilemma. If stock commercial vehicles are insufficiently protected, stock military vehicles are too military for some police forces; they do not wish to appear on the streets in multi-wheeled armoured cars with heavy guns, nor in tracked vehicles, since anything of the sort will be immediately labelled a 'tank' by the media, with all the repressive overtones that go with it. Two types of vehicle are needed: firstly a car which looks standard but is better protected than standard; and secondly a heavier vehicle which, without being overtly antagonistic, gives an air of authority and invulnerability.

Similar demands have arisen within commercial companies, particularly those handling valuable and attractive goods such as banks, jewellers, drug companies and so forth. Their goods need the protection of a discreetly armoured vehicle, and their executives need the protection of an invisibly armoured limousine.

In order to keep the expense within reasonable limits these vehicles have to have a commercial chassis strong enough to carry the weight and put up with the rigours of service, and successful enough to have generated a wide network of spares and repair agencies. Such names as Land Rover, Mercedes, Renault, Iveco and Unimog come to the fore in this context. Then comes the question of design for the particular role, and then the business of providing the requisite protection, and there is rather more to this than welding on layers of steel and fitting bullet-proof glass in the windows. True, steel and glass do have to be added, and so do layers of aramid bullet-proof fibre, self-sealing fuel tanks, run-flat tyres and various other adornments, but all these add up to a considerable increase in weight and therefore the first requirement is to strengthen the suspension and springing; the brakes also need attention, since they are going to have more mass to stop; the steering will very likely require adjustment as a result of the new suspension - whatever is done will generate something else that needs doing. After that the level of protection has to be determined by asking what the customer expects to be assailed with. A 9 mm pistol? A 7.62 mm high-velocity rifle? A .50 Browning machine gun? Land mines? Only when this is determined can the question of armouring begin. There is no quick and easy way to success in this procedure, though in the early days several people were under that impression and consequently are now working at other trades.

With the executive limousine there is the added complication that the finished article should be indistinguishable from the standard unarmoured vehicle, which means careful matching of the suspension heights and superlative finish on the outside. Indeed with some of these vehicles it is possible to climb inside and take a seat without noticing anything out of the ordinary, and in the hands of a good driver no differences will be apparent during ordinary progress. But if the progress is suddenly impeded by villains, then all sorts of things come to light, depending upon the ingenuity of the individual vehicle-builder. Smoke screens, oil slicks, gun-ports, and even more exotic devices come into play as the villains are thwarted.

Specialised police vehicles also begin with a strengthened commercial chassis, but what happens thereafter is ruled more by convenience than cosmetics. It matters little if the shape is changed from the standard; what matters is the amount of protection, the amount of equipment and the number of men you intend to put into the vehicle. Again, protection starts with an assessment of the threat, but this may be more difficult than in the case of private security vehicles, because police can never know what might happen tomorrow. As a result they tend towards worst-case scenarios and armouring against the major threats. They also require highly specialised equipment capable of meeting all sorts of problems, so that the vehicle equipment, to some extent, needs to be modularised so that it can be taken off and something else substituted; thus the same vehicle might be fitted with riot shields this week and have them removed next week.

Armament is a vexed question; in general British police do without fixed armament, but in other countries other policies exist. Not all will go to the extent of the French Gendarmerie Nationale who have a number of AMX six-wheel armoured reconnaissance vehicles armed with 90 mm high-velocity guns, but certainly machine gun cupolas are a common enough fitting in many

This may look line a normal BMW, but it is actually fully armoured and capable of resisting attack by submachine guns, rifles or grenades.

An Alvis mine-resistant patrol vehicle. This will withstand 10kg of TNT detonated underneath it, and can limp home on three wheels if one is blown off. The occupants will be shaken up but uninjured.

countries. For riots, a different type of weapon is demanded, and in many countries the chosen instrument is the water cannon, another highly specialised vehicle.

Perhaps the most highly specialised are the mine-resistant vehicles (MRVs), of which, so far, there are few. This is because almost all the research into this technology has been confined to one country, South Africa, and their expertise is now beginning to percolate to other countries confronted with the mine problem. But as well as being mine-resistant, they also have the virtue of being resistant to explosions from almost any direction, and they have been proved as a safe method of checking out suspect car bombs. Even if the MRV is alongside the bomb when it goes off, the occupants are likely to survive the encounter without serious injuries.

A short wheelbase Alvis MRV delivers a riot squad.

Shorts S52 Armoured Patrol Car UK

The **S52** was designed to provide a well-protected patrol vehicle for use in urban or rural areas in situations which demand protected fire-power but which do not justify a highly expensive and sophisticated military-type armoured fighting vehicle. It carries a crew of three, driver and commander in the cab and a gunner in the manually-rotated turret, with off-duty seating in the body behind the commander. There is also ample room for communications equipment and other stores.

Various weapons can be mounted in the turret, but preference is given to the 7.62 mm FN MAG general-purpose machine gun. Smoke grenade dischargers can also be fitted to the turret if required. An optical periscope acts as a viewing device and also as a sight for the machine gun, and for night operation a searchlight, mounted on the turret, is synchronised with the machine gun in bearing and elevation.

The windscreen is protected by armoured visors which drop down and carry laminated glass inserts to provide sufficient forward vision for driving; alternatively, armoured glass windscreens can be fitted. The interior is lined with insulation, and ventilation or air-conditioning is provided. In addition to the cab doors, emergency exits are provided in the turret roof and in the rear end of the body.

Manufacturers: Short Brothers, Belfast, Northern Ireland

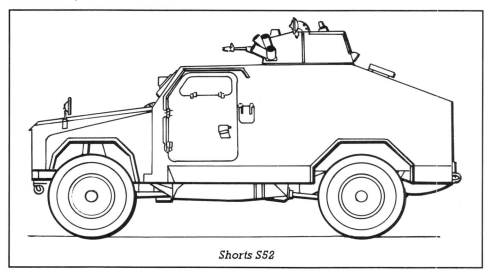

Shorts S52

128

The Shorts S52 armoured patrol car with turret carrying grenade launchers and machine gun.

Shorland S55 Patrol Car UK

Like many vehicles in this field, the **Shorland** is based upon the Land Rover chassis (hence the name: Shorts and Land Rover) which means a worldwide spares and service facility at economic prices. The **S55** was specifically developed for the movement of security forces in high-risk areas, providing good armoured protection and a comfortable interior so as to minimise fatigue for the eight occupants. In order to allow defensive or retaliatory action, eight gunports are provided, through which shotguns or submachine guns can be used, and a searchlight is fitted on the roof. Optional extras include a roof hatch machine gun mounting and smoke grenade dischargers.

The body of the vehicle has been designed on the basis of practical experience; there is, for example, a gutter under the junction of the windscreen and hood so that burning petrol from a hand-thrown bomb will be diverted to the ground without entering the engine compartment, and the roof is slightly ridged so that any bomb landing there will roll off. Run-flat tyres are standard, the radiator is protected by armoured shuttering, and the windscreen can be covered by an armoured shield with vision blocks.

There is a good interior ventilation system, and air-conditioning is available for vehicles destined for hot climates. There are two rear doors and two side doors, and all occupants have seat belts to hold them safely during violent manoeuvres or when travelling across country.

Manufacturer: Short Brothers, Belfast, Northern Ireland

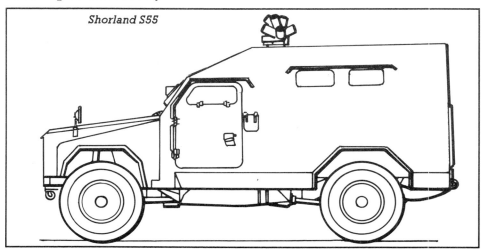

Shorland S55

The Shorland S55 armoured patrol car.

Glover Riot Control Vehicle

Riot control vehicles come in all shapes and sizes, and Glover Webb (now part of the GKN organisation) manufactured this particular model on a Land Rover chassis.

Protection levels from 9 mm pistols to 7.62 mm rifles can be provided as required, and the floor is reinforced to protect against grenades and improved explosive devices. All vision areas are protected to the same level as the bodywork and are additionally protected by grilles. It can carry the driver, vehicle commander, and six fully equipped men; as these men leave via the rear door they can form up behind foldout full height riot shields on each side of the vehicle. There are two hinged opening roof hatches, smoke grenade launchers at the front of the roof, a protected searchlight operated from inside the vehicle, and a public address system.

Right: *Rear of the Glover riot control vehicle.*

Manufacturer: Glover Webb Ltd, Hamble, England

The Glover riot control vehicle showing the side riot shields in use.

Glover FAST Vehicle Group

The **FAST** (Firearms and Special Tactics) vehicle was developed to meet the need of various UK police forces for a low-profile armoured vehicle for special incidents. Each vehicle is designed and built to meet the special requirements of the particular force but they are generally built to have a multi-role capability, provide a very high level of protection against various forms of attack, and yet have a non-aggressive and even homely appearance to the public.

There are two basic body forms, the hardtop and the station wagon. Both are built upon a basic Land Rover structure by fitting a monocoque armoured hull covering front, sides, rear floor and roof to provide protection against high-velocity rifle fire and other small arms ballistic attack. The design is such that the basic dimensions remain the same as the standard Land Rover vehicle and, of course, spare parts and maintenance present few problems anywhere in the world. The hardtop version has three access doors - one each side and one rear - while the station wagon has five doors.

Standard equipment includes run-flat tyres, explosion-suppressed fuel tank, air conditioning and an 'entryphone' allowing the occupants to talk to people outside the vehicle without compromising their own safety. Optional extras include fire suppression systems, spotlights, gunports, special security door-locking, window grilles and several other security accessories.

Manufacturer: Glover Webb Ltd, Hamble, England

The Glover FAST vehicle on a hardtop chassis.

134

Transsac GS Armoured IS Vehicle

This vehicle was based on a chassis designed by the Stonefield company and armoured by Glover Webb. It has full all-terrain capability, and the armour protection is designed to withstand attack by 7.62mm NATO rifle bullets at point blank range. The floor has been reinforced in order to resist hand grenades or petrol bombs thrown beneath the vehicle, and the diesel engine, radiator and fuel tank are fully protected against ballistic attack or fire-bombs. There is a halogen fire extinguishing system, the body apertures are protected against liquid attack, and the run-flat tyres will carry the vehicle 50km after being punctured.

The rear section has side and rear entry doors and can carry 12 men in comfort. It is fully air-conditioned and is also provided with vision blocks and gun ports on the sides and rear. Optional equipment includes additional gun ports and vision blocks, a roof hatch with machine gun mounting, window grilles, light bars and spotlights, smoke grenade launchers and communications equipment.

Manufacturer: Transsac International, Crawley, England

The Transsac GS 4 x 4 vehicle with air conditioning and protective grilles.

Glover Thracian Command Vehicle UK

Public disorders generally demand a great deal of police presence, all of which some senior officer has to control; he can do this much better if he is provided with a special vehicle containing all the necessary command and communications equipment. The **Glover Thracian** is a good example of this sort of vehicle and the design allows a great deal of individuality so that security forces can tailor it to their own particular equipment and requirements. It can be armoured or not, as preferred, and is usually divided into three sections: the cab, a radio compartment with side-door access, and a command compartment with access from the rear. The radio compartment has room for all types of radio, facsimile, telex, encrypt/decrypt and television equipment, while the command compartment can be equipped with whatever can fit into it and is deemed necessary. Lights, sirens, air-conditioning and similar ancillary equipment can be provided.

Manufacturer: Glover Webb Ltd, Hamble, England

Below left: *The Glover Thracian command vehicle with video camera and microwave link on the roof.*

Below right: *A view inside the command compartment of the Thracian vehicle.*

Hotspur Hussar IS Vehicle UK

The **Hotspur Hussar** was designed as a military armoured personnel carrier in 1984, but since then a number of variant models have appeared, covering such applications as communications vehicle, ambulance, prisoner transport and EOD tender.

The **Hussar** is based upon Land Rover components, using a third driven axle to provide a 6x6 configuration with space, excellent cross-country performance and a high payload. The **Hussar** is capable of carrying a crew of two and ten fully-equipped passengers over country which many 4x4 vehicles would find impassable.

The standard internal security vehicle has folding seats for 12 men in the rear section, six down each side, and is provided with three gun ports on each side and one in each of the rear doors, each port having an armoured vision block above it. The driver and commander have louvred shutters which give a protection to their bullet-proof windshield and side glass. All options, such as air-conditioning, roof turret, machine gun mounts, searchlights, smoke dischargers and fire extinguishing systems can be provided as required by the particular operator.

Manufacturer: Hotspur Armoured Products, Dumfries, Scotland

Below left: The Hotspur Hussar internal security vehicle.

Below right: Inside the Hotspur Hussar.

Boneschi MRAV

The **MRAV** (Multi-Role Armoured Vehicle) is based on a Fiat chassis, fitted with a powerful diesel engine, making a vehicle with good cross-country performance and ample room inside to carry up to 12 men in comparative comfort and with room for more in an emergency. The body is of ballistic steel armour, the sides being 6mm thick, and all windows and vision blocks are of 38mm glass to provide the same degree of protection against attack as the steel hull. Side and rear doors give access to the crew compartment, all doors being provided with anti-intrusion locks, and the compartment has three vision blocks and gun ports on each side and one in the rear door.

Optional equipment includes: anti-tear gas filtering, air-conditioning, runflat tyres, heating, central fire extinguishing and communications equipment systems. Standard fittings include rifle racks and equipment storage.

Right: The Boneschi MRAV4 Multi-Role Armoured Vehicle is in wide use among Italian police forces.

Manufacturer:
Carrozzeria Boneschi, Cambiago, Italy

These highly specialised vehicles are built upon a number of different commercial chassis selected to suit the tactical requirement and hence the weight of water and equipment which has to be carried. All vehicles are basically a chassis carrying a cab with remote controls for the water cannon; one or two water cannon; tanks for water, dye and tear-gas; and two engines, one to propel the vehicle and the other to operate the pumps supplying liquid to the cannon.

The cannon itself may be either a simple nozzle delivering a continuous stream of water, or a 'pulse-jet' device which launches 'slugs' of 7 to 10 litres of water instead of a continuous stream, a system which reduces water consumption by about 25 percent. Some versions permit operation in either mode. The water is delivered to the cannon at about 1800 litres per minute by a pump, and a mixing unit allows dyestuff and/or tear-gas to be added to the water. The dyestuff allows the rioters to be marked by the water so that they can be subsequently identified, and the addition of tear-gas at a very low dilution adds a further degree of discomfort to the water douche.

In addition to the basic equipment outlined above, these vehicles can be fitted with riot shields, bulldozer blades, lights, sirens, communications equipment, smoke and tear-gas grenade launchers and so forth. The larger vehicles also incorporate a separate, raised, cab for the water cannon operators.

Manufacturer: Various

Water cannon awaiting delivery to a European police force.

RG-38 Bastion Armoured Transport South Africa

The **RG-38** has been designed as an armoured cash carrier but has obvious applications in other roles where a secure armoured vehicle of compact size is required. It has been developed upon a chassis specially made by TFM because most existing armoured transit vehicles are based upon commercial chassis, and these fall into two groups, 2.5 ton and 5 ton. A 2.5 ton chassis, once armoured, has a relatively low payload, whilst a 5 ton produces a vehicle which is somewhat bulky for urban driving. The special TFM chassis provides a compact vehicle with an unladen weight of 3.1 tonnes and a payload of 750kg.

TFM supply the vehicle either fully built, with a ballistic steel armoured body and bullet-proof windows, or as a chassis with the armoured nose and windscreen frame in place, after which the purchaser can complete the vehicle to his own requirements. Either type is supplied with a 5-cyl diesel engine and run-flat tyres as standard.

The RG-38 Bastion cash transport vehicle from South Africa.

Manufacturer:
TFM Ltd, Olifantsfontein, South Africa

140

TM 170 Armoured Personnel Carrier Germany

Like most light armoured vehicles the **TM 170** begins on a basis of a commercial chassis, in this case the Unimog cross-country vehicle. This is then provided with a welded armour steel hull giving protection to 7.62 mm NATO level. The driver and commander sit in front, their windscreen being protected by two armoured shutters which fold down on to the engine hood when not in use. Both men have three roof-mounted periscopes to give them observation to front and side when the shutters are in place. Their side windows also have steel shutters, and each man has a roof hatch.

Ten fully equipped men can ride in the troop compartment, on individual seats down each side. There is a door in each side, behind the driving compartment, with a gun port in each door. There is also an entrance hatch in the rear of the hull carrying a gun port and vision block. On each side of the hull are two windows with bullet-proof glass, and there is a large circular hatch in the roof.

The military version of the **TM 170**, used, for example, by the German Border Guards, is fully amphibious, using water jets and the paddle action of the wheels to swim. The police and security version is not amphibious. The usual range of additional features - lights, sirens, communications equipment, smoke grenade dischargers and so forth is available.

Manufacturer:
Thyssen Maschinenbau, Witten, Germany

The Police version of the Thyssen TM 170 armoured personnel carrier.

The **VAB/VMO** (Vehicule l'Avant Blindé/ Vehicule de Maintien de l'Ordre) was developed in France for export to those countries who required an exceptionally powerful and versatile public order vehicle. The **VAB** (Forward Area Armoured Vehicle) was originally developed as a military reconnaissance vehicle in the early 1970s and was developed by the Renault group in conjunction with Saviem and with armour developed by Creusot-Loire. With the various shifts and changes in French armament production, it now falls under the Giat Industries group. Some 4000 have been delivered to the French Army in four and six-wheel versions, and a wide range of variants, of which the **VMO** is one, were then developed by Renault. Standing some 6 metres long, 2.5 metres wide and 2.1 high, and weighing 13 tonnes, the **VAB** is an impressive and intimidating vehicle, and its mere appearance can frequently cause a riot to dissolve.

The **VMO** takes the basic armoured hull as a starting point and then fits a TOI (Tourelle de l'Observation et Intervention) cupola on top. This is provided with bullet-proof and mesh-screened side windows giving excellent visibility and can carry grenade launchers, a machine gun, video cameras and similar equipment.

Alternatively, or in addition, to the TOI turret, a Tourelle de l'Observation et Intervention cupola can also be fitted on the roof. This is an armoured turret with a 7.62 mm general-purpose machine gun and with storage for 4000 rounds of belted ammunition; it also has six observation periscopes and a tilting head sighting periscope, and a searchlight and grenade launcher can also be mounted.

Other armament options include the

TLI-127 cupola, an armoured turret carrying a .50 Browning machine gun; the STBV rotating open shield with 7.62 mm machine gun; the CB52 three-sided shielded barbette with 7.62 mm machine gun; and the SCR semicircular 'skate rail' carrying a 7.62 mm machine gun.

The **VAB** is completely amphibious, being propelled in the water by two steerable water-jet units mounted at the rear corners, with automatic bilge pumps to deal with any water which may enter the hull through faulty door seals. The rear compartment can carry ten men, with the driver and vehicle commander in the forward cab. The engine air intake is protected against burning fuel from petrol bombs and the exhaust and fuel fillers are protected from damage or interference. Optional equipment can include: a bulldozer blade; a 'crowd-pusher' blade, which can be 2.5 m wide; a foldable blade which can open to 7.5 m width; a towing winch; public address system; lights; sirens and camera equipment; a tear-gas dispenser and a special device for removing paint from the windshield.

There is also a variant model known as the **VAB/PC** which is fitted out as a command and communications vehicle. Both the VMO and PC are available in 4 x 4 or 6 x 6 configuration.

Manufacturer:
Giat Industries, Versailles, France

Opposite: Renault VAB/VMO in arctic dress, with TOI cupola and shielded

Below: Renault VAB/VMO fitted with TOI cupola and bulldozer blade

Glossary

Access Control: A system of supervising the entrances to and exits from any building or area so that only authorised personnel can enter or leave it. It may then be sub-divided so that entrance to particular sections can be restricted to selected personnel.

Bi-ocular: An eyepiece unit which allows the use of both eyes to view the output of a single optical axis. As opposed to **Binocular**, in which two separate eyepieces view two separate optical axes; this permits stereoscopic viewing to provide the appearance of depth in the field of view; bi-ocular instruments do not provide such an appearance.

Biometric: An access control system which is based upon the recognition of physical features to allow admission; for example, comparing the face of the applicant with a photograph stored in computer memory, or comparing a fingerprint with fingerprint.

Bore-sighting: Ensuring that the axis of a weapon sight is in correct alignment with the axis of the weapon's barrel, so that sight and weapon point at the same place.

Card reader: An access control device which reads electronic information carried on a magnetic stripe card, compares it with the records stored in computer memory and then admits or rejects the applicant.

Collimating sight: A type of weapon sight which uses optical effects to superimpose a sighting mark upon the view of the target. May be used with one or both eyes open, and, within certain limits, is not dependent upon the position of the firer's eye.

Conveyorised: An X-ray machine for examining baggage which uses a motor-driven belt to carry the baggage through the path of the X-ray, so ensuring a steady and correct speed to ensure thorough examination.

Disruptor: A firearm-type device for firing a projectile into an explosive device so as to cut wires, wreck a timing device, or disconnect the batteries at high speed and before the firing device can function.

Doppler radar: Radar which detects moving targets by displaying only returning signals which are at a higher or lower frequency than that of the transmitted signal. This change in frequency is a result of adding or subtracting the speed of the target's movement to or from the speed of the radar signal.

EOD: Explosive Ordnance Disposal.

Eye-safe: A laser which is not powerful enough to cause damage if inadvertently aimed into the human eye.

Fibre-optic: A method of transmitting signals through a glass-fibre filament, using light as the medium.

IED: Improvised Explosive Device; a 'home-made bomb'.

Image intensification: An electro-optical system which detects minute differences in light and shade in a poorly-lit scene and electronically amplifies these differences to make the scene recognisable.

Interrogator: Unit in an access control system which queries the identity of an applicant, either by studying physical characteristics, reading a magnetic card or other means.

LED: Light Emitting Diode. Signal lamps used on various types of equipment.

Manipulator: A 'mechanical hand' on the end of a jointed arm, carried on EOD robots, and capable of twisting, bending, gripping and generally performing most tasks possible by a human hand, but under remote control.

Perimeter Protection: A system designed to keep intruders out of a building or area. May be active, eg by using fences and barriers, or passive, by using video, radar or infra-red to detect intruders.

Piezo-electric: An electrical circuit which depends upon a sensitive crystal which, when pressure is applied, generates electricity.

PIN: Personal Identification Number.

Sniffer: An electronic device which samples air and detects the presence of chemical vapours.

Thermal imaging: An electro-optical system for detecting minute differences in temperature in a viewed area and translating them so as to form a coherent picture.

Transducer: A device which reacts to a physical stimulus - eg pressure, temperature, noise - and converts it into an electrical signal.

UTM: Universal Transverse Mercator; a system of map referencing.

Video link: A radio link between camera and monitor screen which delivers video images.

Windage: Lateral adjustment of a weapon sight to compensate for the effect of a cross-wind.